THE SUFFOLK LIBRARY

The Green Bond

The Green Bond

ADRIAN BELL

THE BOYDELL PRESS · IPSWICH

Published by Boydell Press Ltd
PO Box 24 Ipswich 1P1 1JJ
First published 1976

ISBN 0 85115 066 7

Printed in Great Britain by
Northumberland Press Limited
Gateshead

'YOU want shoeing,' he said, and rummaged in a box. He brought out a new rubber and fitted it to the end of my fraying stick. I paid, and departed with a silent third foot.

Today heaven smiled on me on my seat on the cobblestones under flowering cherries. I come to Bungay to stroll and sketch—and to dream. It is my holiday. The proprietor of the old curiosity shop was sunning himself before his open door. A garden in a cul-de-sac was a banquet of tulips; red and yellow, full blown and gently swaying in a breeze from under a dimpled formation of cloud. They were saying, 'It's been a good party, and though we may be a bit unsteady now, we are ready for one more toast to the lordly sun.'

I strolled to a seat by the churchyard of St. Mary's, whose acre or two of new-mown grass exuded a vernal smell. Opposite me stood the Fleece Inn. I admired the building and the one next door to it, which is now the Employment Office, with a central Vanbrugh window. It must once have housed a grandee with a shimmering equipage. I would have touched my forelock to such a one. Indeed I would. Damn all this 'equality'. It would have been my pride to have been a pre-Enclosure peasant, such as wore silver buckles on his shoes on Sundays, according to Cobbett.

As St. Mary's clock struck noon I noticed the image of a dodderer who had just risen, reflected in a great blank window of the Vanbrugh mansion: he was poking a stick in front of him. By God, it was me! I sank back on my seat. That bushy hair, that shambling stance. Something must be done. I rose again with resolve. I dropped my rubber-ended stick. I went into a barber's shop. 'My hair looks awful,' I told the barber. 'No—venerable,' he replied, plying his scissors nevertheless. Next I swore by the nine gods never again would I wear these ancient trousers except in the garden. I squared my shoulders: I strode into The Fleece. I ordered a pint of bitter. A half-pint is a toy: a pint is a test. I lifted it to my lips and no drop spilt. So a man's a man for a' that.

The effect was not what I had intended. Hirsutely and sartorially reformed, I called with a cabbage (rare joy of being one jump ahead on the vegetable plot) and to pick up a week's supply of breakfast eggs, marked Mon., Tues., Wed., etc., because I like a bit of reading on my breakfast egg. Our egg-lady, Sighile (the old Irish equivalent of Sheila, pronounced Siheelee), cried, 'Dear man, what have you done to yourself! Your hair—where is it?' ('On the barber's floor,' I said.) 'And your gipsy trousers? And why the presidential white linen jacket? And these cavalry twills carved round your legs? Where is your gnarled ash stick, with which you stood so characteristically with both hands on the crook looking at the ground, thinking?

'Oh, happy wanderer arriving over the fields, who filled my sun-porch with scents of wild thyme off your clothes

2

when you had crossed the brook and clambered up the bank! Where are those gipsy trousers, those rebellious locks...? Can't you understand we like you like that? You haven't burnt them, have you?'

'The trousers? Not yet.'

'Gipsy trousers are for ever. How old, actually?'

'Twenty years; three of them in the stable as cast-aways, to be cut up for rags: but retrieved, waistband mended by devoted spouse, many times washed to a ghost of themselves.'

'You and I are peasants,' she said. 'We are the past, but we are also England's future, after the Hour of Truth, which is soon, and the death of money. Then for the day of nettle juice, grass juice, wild thyme, impregnating gipsy skirts and peasant trousers, and "many a green gown", hand-sewn every button, every stitch. Oh, lovely old velvet jacket that hung round your shoulders like a goodwife-dear, your wavy straw hat with a buttercup drooping from the brim. Jog on the footpath way, grapple cocksfoot and comfrey to drag yourself out of ditches, arrive here with goose-grass on your sleeves, shoes gilded with buttercups, or mired, no matter which. Oh, Adrian Bell, never look at yourself in a great blank window of an Employment Office again.'

❧ ❧ ❧ ❧ ❧ ❧

'PLANTED POTATOES.' Full stop. Thus on the calendar which hangs on the wall. Is that all? By no means. Think of the names: Arran Pilot, Majestic, Desirée ... Pas de Desirée: why should I desert my old favourites of our sceptred isle?

3

Think of the methods of planting a potato patch; by spade, by dibble, or by hacking out a deep trench and standing each seed potato ('should be size of a pullet's egg'. Isn't.) upright in it. Clever the man who can get ten little potatoes standing upright in open order in that trench without one or other fainting on parade.

The trench is not straight because I hack it out by eye with swan-necked hoe: earth mounds up to right and left. The first attempt looks like a map of this lane; surely the original 'rolling English road'. Then the measuring, or 'mensuration' as our school books liked to call it. Fifteen inches between tubers, 2 ft. 6 in. between rows. How to measure 2 ft. 6 in. by boot on foot or eye in head? Boot measures (with earthy accretions) 1 ft. Placing boots heel to toe, foxlike, on rough earth is staggering: it can be done, but tends to look like a ritual dance.

I have come to the stage in life when a man invents a non-bending technique of potato-planting. A stout walking-stick does for dibble. My walnut tree flung one at me in a gale, complete with rough crook; it has become a friend. Where the ground gets tougher I take the iron bar called a 'fold drift' which has outlasted many shepherds' lives, making holes for hurdle stakes. It is a gardener's treasure. Next comes the game of plugging each hole with a potato from the height dictated by a moderately stiff back. It is as dicey as darts; but after 140 potato 'bombs' delivered on target I call myself an expert.

By the time the ground was dry enough to tread on, my seed potatoes in their trays had grown stalk-eyes and looked like little green men from Mars. They had been rather getting on my nerves, as if they would soon begin to crawl. But by the end of this day of planting I straightened my bowed but not quite bent back, heaved up my iron bar and parked it in its corner with the well-known clang.

How all our tools have their voices, as soon as you want to take one down: there is the altercation of the wire rake with a cultivating tool, and the 'blast you!' of a sleeping bow-saw as it rocks on its nail. This is a new wire rake, and has a curious 'ha-ha-ha' which I thought of last Sunday when the hymn bade us 'strike with joy your golden lyres'.

So, having raked and tidied my potato patch, I went indoors and wrote with a ballpoint and earthy fingers 'Potatoes planted' in the calendar, and that was that.

Not quite. In pocketing some loose change I encountered yet one more spud, wrinkled as a centenarian. It had been recommended as a cure for rheumatism, following the failure of the copper bracelet. I had come on a group of major-generals comparing each other's bracelets, an unusual spectacle of proud and virile men, until I discovered it was not a vanity but a hoped-for-cure. The wife of one of them confided to me that the thing bit into her back in bed.

After vainly wearing this slave bangle I met a man who produced from his pocket a potato, as hard as a stone. 'After three days I could clap my hands above my head,' he claimed. I presumed his rheumatism had flowed into the potato and fossilised it. But mine was a non-conductor of rheum and merely looked wizened and sad. It sits on my mantelshelf; no more to masquerade as a purseful of pennies in my trouser pocket. Shall I plant it? POTATO PARK FULL: not an inch to spare. And I have stooped enough for the day. I need relief by walking with expanded lungs, taking a staff as tall as my shoulder for pace-maker.

So let's go: forget the 140 stalk-eyed babies abed in the earth. They are going to cause a lot of work yet; but for the moment I can forget them. Forget rheumatism. Come on, left-right: four miles heel-and-toe is better than a potato in the pocket. From High Common to Blacksmith's Common to Mill Common to St. John's churchyard which I love for the bronzed limbs of its wind-wrung pines, each one a Samson praying for a last strength to bring down the Philistines; also for its hoard of peaceful sleep bequeathed to my yet earth-loitering soul by the forefathers of this parish. But most of all to see how the wild strawberry is doing that blooms under the step of the churchyard gate.

※　　※　　※　　※　　※　　※

'COME ROUND the oak tree,' she said, 'where we can step into the field and pick primroses.'

The 'step' was over a strand of wire which had sagged, surrendered, buried its barbs in grass and earth. It even gave the instep a spring. She held out a helping hand. I was in the field, on the grassy brow of ploughland, called 'brew' in the Suffolk tongue.

'You looked weary,' she told me, 'when you suddenly came in sight. Even forlorn. I didn't recognise you.'

I had walked the roundabout way, over commons, through two churchyards. I had noted a row of head-

6

stones three deep: 'Green ... Green ... Green ... Beloved wife of ... Beloved daughter ...' In the other one were table tombs to whole families, tables now bearing great helpings of ivy, 'erected by sorrowing relatives ... 1829 ... 1834 ...'

Sorrow evaporates: gladness of primroses resurrects, springs up for love of life, or for love itself; pistils, styles, 'thrum-eyed' or 'pin-eyed' awaiting pollinating insects, guarded by nature against self-fertilisation, quite elaborately guarded. Those simple-seeming flower faces staring at the sky are expecting primrose fulfilment, primrose seed, primrose offspring.

I had walked and walked. I was feeling tired now in body but somewhat refreshed in mind as I came up the slope of Mill Common. Here I knew I could rest awhile on Sighile's veranda in the sun which today was spring-like, and have a cup of tea before taking the road for home. I value the friendship for which that basket chair stands hospitably on the veranda.

She had been digging. She had dug a big bed into a black surge of tilth, reminding me of the first wild ferment of our homebrew. A camera misses the subtlety of digging: the painter cannot paint it. My joy in the country can be a joy in the sight of good digging, of good ploughing. What's that fellow standing there for, gazing into vacancy? What indeed?

And having dug ... 'I thought I would pick a bunch of primroses to have on my tray with my tea,' she said. Living alone, she makes friends of light and life. 'And then I saw someone coming up the slope just about where the old post-mill stood, planting a staff before him, like a pilgrim.'

7

I said, 'In tramping often over Great Common I have become familiar with its ghosts: they are tinkers, tinmen, pedlars, Petulengros, and many many horses. Sometimes I walk toward a broad and brooding sky there, full of tender fire, so that I am moved to exclaim with Elisha, "Behold the chariots of Israel and the horsemen thereof." The Bible has a speech for every experience.'

'You looked older,' she said. She stooped to a host of primroses in the ditch, and I stood on the grass verge. 'As if your thoughts were a load on your back.' She handed up to me a primrose bud which looked like a thin green crayon with a yellow point. 'Now you look younger.'

I followed along the headland while she dived and climbed; watched her fingers folding themselves around stems of open flowers, then carefully snapping the stalk of a bud at its longest, or coaxing from its base the rough, stiff positive green of a leaf, and slipping it round her posy as a sheath.

I said, looking across to the common where 'Stone Cottages' had once stood, 'We must learn more of that John Davy and the spring he found, which is said to be ten yards from a certain ash tree, and he sunk a bottomless barrel on the spot, and it was for a well, which had water when all other wells were dry; a sort of miracle, I suppose.'

She agreed. 'But isn't primrosing in today's sunshine better than researching into the histories of men in tombs?' And she thrust her posy under my nose. Its faint sweet smell transformed me for a moment into a child again and compelled me to agree.

After reading tombs I discovered I was still alive.

'When one is alive one *is* alive and goes on with the living,' said Dr. Frank Leavis the other day; the same man who said of me in my early thirties, 'Adrian Bell is naïve, but he is naïve in the right way.' I told the primroses of it. 'Like you I am naïve: like you I am alive.' While we are alive, we live also through things called insensate; petals, knots in wood. We are friends through our wildwood friends: it is a green bond: a bud is a word: the spider in his beaded web is a wizard.

Sighile had finished her primrose-picking, and emerged from the ditch. I was sitting on my raincoat leaning against a large hollow oak, surveying a wide view. I said to her, 'If I could camp in this hollow tree, and look through its ever open doorway in the morning, I should feel that all the world were mine—even as you felt once, you told me, when you spread a rug in front of your caravan for yourself and your small children, and putting your arms around them cried, "The world is yours, my darlings, and its primroses for you to pick."'

❧ ❧ ❧ ❧ ❧ ❧

THE GORSE has been in bloom all this mild winter, and now begins to look brilliant, even profligate. I return in thought to Amaryllis and the golden gorse of that spring which introduced the long hot summer of 1921.

I first saw her bending to auriculas which she was planting in her garden. She was the new schoolmistress. I was then a young farmer of 20. My garden consisted of one round bed in some hen-worried grass. Amaryllis (her parents got it from a book) came over one evening and planted it with some of her auriculas. I have loved them ever since.

She taught me to sketch, in a fashion; a hobby I have only taken up again lately. We lived opposite each other, she beside the school. In the quiet after the children had dispersed, we would pause at our gates and chat. One May Day she and I took sandwiches and cycled toward the sun, which was seaward. The gorse was all golden that year. Never had it been gayer. We stopped at an inn on our way. She had a stone ginger beer, I had an old-and-mild, farm men's favourite drink then. Then we sketched the thatched inn from the churchyard opposite. Her drawing was careful, mine a scribble. Yet I guessed I was going to love mine, because it would be a souvenir of our 'golden gorse day'—and so it proved.

From a seat before the inn we surveyed a hazy river valley: some fairly young poplars and a sweep of green vacancy. I took up my pad. 'Amaryllis, where do I begin? It eludes definition.'

'Don't begin,' she said. 'Let it be. It's our holiday. Treat it as a mirage, a loveliness of nothingness.'

'Even the clouds look solider,' I agreed. 'Like floury dumplings on plates of pewter shadow,' she mused.

'That's good,' I cried, and got to work. 'Hold on to dumplings; whitest, flouriest dumplings from your mother's pot. Amaryllis, can you make dumplings like that?'

'Oh, Farmer Boy.' (She called me that, I being three years younger than her, which I tried to forget.) 'Oh, Farmer Boy, what a personal question to ask a school-mistress!' She seemed to flush under her straw hat which let through flecks of sunlight on her face. My clouds began to look worried. 'I'm getting hungry,' I said.

We cycled on to find a picnic site. She slowed suddenly and looked aside. We had come to a small, sad-looking cottage.

'Do you know someone who lives here?' I asked, dismounting. She nodded. I looked around. 'She's not at home,' I told her.

'It was a "he",' she muttered.

'Oh.' My heart was mined like sand in an egg-timer.

We pedalled on in silence. A cloud like a flatiron flung a few drops at us. The sun blazed again just as we came to a heath of gorse in full bloom. 'How lovely!' she exclaimed, breaking our spell of silence.

We propped our bikes, and stooped and dodged among gorse, which suddenly sloped away. We found ourselves on the lip of an enormous crater of gorse. It had been a gravel pit; now it was like a huge bowl of molten gold. Larks lifted out of it, trembling and trilling. A mat of grass just wide enough for two offered itself. We sat down to our picnic. Amaryllis seemed muted. 'Wonderful all this gorse,' I said, puzzled as to what had become of that 'Oh, how lovely!' of hers. My hand touched her arm. The arm stayed statue-still. 'Who was he?' I asked.

Suddenly Amaryllis burst into rapid speech, telling me who he was, what he was, his virtues, his ... She checked herself, went on quietly. Her friend she called him: her 'friend' distinctly. Bill. Bill who? She shook off his surname as irrelevant. There had been weekly meetings, occasionally at hers, mostly at his. She conjured to me a tea table set beside a log fire, a big chair ... 'A big armchair?' I suggested. Her reticence became quite awesome. 'A chair for two?' I dared. She nodded, now utterly

11

silent. He had lost a young wife after only a year. She had ... died, run away? I dared not ask further. He was desperately sad, she said.

Her mother became ill, and Amaryllis had to cope at home, before and after school. There was a gap. Bill had begun drinking, she was told by a friend. And he was taking out a girl he had met in a bar. Amaryllis was indignant. She wrote and said she would see him no more if it were true. He did not reply. His cottage was found to be locked; and he was gone.

Thank God for that, I thought. Then Amaryllis said, 'I got a letter this morning. He's coming back. He needs me, he says.' She went on as if talking to herself. 'I ought to have kept him out of bad company. I ought to have understood. I wrote a thoughtless letter: it was cruel.'

'You love him—confess,' She would not in words confess. 'He is my friend,' she kept saying.

We looked at each other: her eyes had green flecks, and their gaze stopped the clock of my heart. She laid a hand on mine. So we stayed in all this gladness of gorse, after all the 'loveliness of nothingness' of the long green valley. 'If you were older ...' she said. She lay back gazing at the clouds. 'You have not suffered.' She closed her eyes: a tear crept under either lid. I leaned over her and took up each tear on my lips. We seemed to drift into an eternity of sleep. I woke to her kneeling over me. 'Time to be on our homeward way, Farmer Boy.'

We crept out of our eyrie, mounted our bikes. The sun was low. As we came by the cottage a small light was visible within. She stopped, almost overbalanced on me, scrambled out of the frame of her machine. She went and tried the door: it was unlocked. She hesitated, ran back to me, flung her arms round me, gave me a sobbing kiss, and vanished into the dark lobby as one who plunges into a black flood. I propped her bike and waited. And waited. At last I mounted my own and went on my way alone.

That was about fifty years ago.

I realise now, though then I only guessed, what is in store for a woman who marries a man to save him from himself. I still have my sketch of the inn. Today I drove all that way from where I live now, remembering the golden gorse in the old gravel pit. Golden gorse was all my company this day. Around our old lair I found now much litter, but our secret place was still unpolluted. As I sat down there, young Amaryllis's face hovered with sudden clarity before me. What is Time? I wondered. Yes, what the devil is it? I recalled the steadfast gaze, green-flecked, which could stop the clock of my heart. How calm our pulses would be now, were we sitting here together. Or would they?

❈ ❈ ❈ ❈ ❈ ❈

ONCE A month there is a service in the little church of Ilketshall St. John at the end of our lane. The church is not yet redundant: the candles do not outnumber the congregation. The service seems to gain something from the three weeks waiting for it.

It was the Sunday for reading the parable of the Vine-yard, which is the code for the counter-revolution. He who worked in the vineyard for an hour got the same

13

pay as he who worked from dawn till dark. It will be an anti-differential revolution, the craftsman's revolution, whose penny is new-minted, a golden poverty. There is a lesson in primroses. They are very complex in their internal organisation; but they are entirely ruled by the Lord of hosts as to their reproductive powers, their deaths, and their resurrections which happen when the Church is fasting.

We sang a few hymns, and a part of the 119th Psalm; kneeled while prayers were said over us, hoped for the best, were commended to God as being worth a blessing, or anyhow needing one. And so the door was opened and the voluntary died into the stir of nature in the mild grey day outside; a cock crowing, a peewit's plaint, a robin's trill.

I attend a church service as I would attend an audit. Balancing my person against my potential, as any craftsman should, I do not find myself too miserably in the red. Fate has us in hand. Fate works in our lives as the Lord of hosts works in the primrose. Some visitant out of the blue is decreed for the primrose. Pismires from Heaven? What visitant, then, to fertilise our powers? What go-between? An angel? That was once a coin. Or one of those 'golden' tiny pennies newly-minted: the widow's mite, or some God-given provision for the widow's cruse, for which a 'golden' penny might be as efficacious a token as the old half-sovereign it mimes? It has some connection with the parable of the Vineyard to my muddled mind. All life being a parable, this is a gesture of it.

I fumbled and dropped a new penny on the ground: my friend picked it up, that new-minted penny. She then picked four primroses and a leaf to fold around them, she being a nimble bender and I unable to touch my toes. We swapped a golden penny for a golden buttonhole. Barter. There's one sort of luck in that: home-made luck. We invoked it when the Banks owned all Suffolk in the 'twenties and strangled up the purse-strings. So many sacks of potatoes for a pig; four cocks for a coomb of corn. It worked; our home-made luck.

'Henceforth I ask not good fortune. I myself am good fortune.' Walt Whitman was a foot-traveller and was singing of that. 'Strong and content I travel the open road.' For myself, call me a footpath man for choice. The kerb-scraping juggernaut cannot take the skin off my knuckles on a country footpath; though I met a beefling there who glared, snorted and fled.

※　　※　　※　　※　　※　　※

'FOUR FEET defines a footpath,' I was told. Is it odd that a path should travel three sides of a field to come to its conclusion? Once yonder house was a pub, and the devious path deviated as straight as farming allows from the church to that pub. Oh, what a sacramental history hast thou, my wayward path. 'Potable sunbeam,' Jefferies called good ale. English ale, as much as red wine from France, can be termed in a true sense sacramental, since life is. After a day in the heat of the old-time harvest, along came the stone jars about 7 p.m.

Said Lord-of-the-harvest Fred, raising the first pint among his royal stacks like a sceptre, 'A pint of beer at seven set a man up.' Whey-faced office-sitters have never known what it was to fork up to the bully-hole great sheaves of the bearded Revetts wheat; the desperate sweat, the triumph of it. They have never lived who lounge in city bars.

Is this a viable footpath, which is signposted as such? I have a footrule: it measures 18 inches of level and 18 inches of slide or dive into a ditch. I lurch on to livery ploughland, get stuck, strive on. My friend looks back. I trip over my shoelace which has come undone. She comes back to me, stoops (easily she stoops) and ties the filthy lace. She has noticed something else. A smile plays furtively: she murmurs something.

'What's that about Hendrick?'

'I'm sorry, I didn't mean you to hear.'

'Who was this Hendrick?' I demand.

'When I took my class for a country walk, little Hendrick always fell behind and got stuck. "Come on, little Hendrick," we called. He grinned and tried again: he tripped. "Go and do up his bootlaces," I told an older girl. "Please, Miss," she called back, "his boots are on the wrong feet." And he could never get the right button through the right buttonhole of his coat.'

'I see,' I said, redistributing the buttons of my raincoat. I managed to grin, Hendrickly, snared in this endless succession of tussock, rooted bramble, and mire. Shoes tight, buttons right, I took a determined stride, was instantly snatched back by my staff which had got sucked deep in a slab of furrow. She tried not to laugh, but laughter gained on her: her throat vibrated. 'But he was a dear little fellow,' she insisted. 'We all loved little Hendrick.' I staggered on. 'Oh, we did.'

At last I gained hard ground. I stood with both hands

16

resting on my staff, gazing from the slope of Manor Farm. 'You look like a sage,' she said. 'Sage of Suffolk,' she there named me. I dragged my sketch-book from a deep pocket in which it was wedged. My buttons again failed to agree with buttonholes. I shook my head. 'I'll settle for Hendrick,' I said.

❀ ❀ ❀ ❀ ❀ ❀

THE FORGE is derelict (but horses will be needed again), and the blacksmith's house is a ruin. Of other housen (they deserve the folk appellation) on the corner of Blacksmith's Common, a friend looking for a home asked, 'Are they for sale?' 'No, for demolition,' I replied. 'A pity,' he commented. 'There is plenty for pity,' I added. Crumbled bricks suddenly regain their rose-colour being fractured.

There are 'luxury' bungalows round by Took's Common (was Took a tinker?), neat but in what sense luxury I do not know. I was once such a fool as to find a sort of luxury in bringing home to our cottage, by a yoke and a hoop, silver-shining zinc pails of spring water. That was a scintillating saunter.

I thought the Blind Cottages were awaiting the same fate as George's forge and home. The Blind Cottages' windows are blanked with tin, hence our name for them. The wind plays ghosts arriving for a party at the right hand front door. A martin's nest is clamped to a bedroom wall: brambles have a foot in a back door.

Lately a flutter of curiosity was roused in us by seeing a For Sale notice stuck on each front door. We paused.

17

A puff of wind swung the door and ushered us in. The price I knew: seven thousand pounds. It looks a long price, written in words. In less than an hour my wife and I had planned the two cottages as one (for whoever was interested), knew exactly where the bathroom was, and the downstairs loo via a cupboard under the stairs through into an annexe which had been E.C.

The Blind Cottages are neo-Georgian; about 1930. The roof is good: a week's grazing for a family of rabbits is in the rear guttering. Rates are going to sink us all, unless the balloon bursts before then and our paper money is swept up as litter. Here one could return to zero rates and zero services and fatten a pig and grow a rood of potatoes, and live mostly on barter as we did in the nineteen-twenties in remote Suffolk, as I well remember.

My wife and I took less than an hour to plan those dwellings: we are pretty good at it, as our family will testify who took one look at our unredeemed present home and pronounced it hopeless. But rates could drive us and many like us out of our Edens, and rating officers with flaming swords will keep us out. To whom then should we sell our old homes? To oil-rig men and helicopter pilots, and that self-proliferating race of executives from the office blocks of cities which produce more reams of typed and duplicated paper than good goods. Ad infinitum: amen.

The Blind Cottages can never be highly rated because they have no water. None? 'Water from well' says the agent's particulars whose 'accuracy cannot be guaranteed' (footnote). I peeped down the rusty iron pump in the middle of the derelict garden. The handle clattered like a disturbed skeleton. 'Water from well': how familiar that sounds to us two; quite like the old days of the yoke and hooped pails.

Is this all you get for seven thousand pounds today? By no means. At what price would you value a Henry Moore sculpture? The first thing you come to when you set foot on this property is a hollow oak. It is very old and was once pollarded. It has unfurled itself into a yard-wide circle: it is just a scroll of rugged bark, but alive. Within, it resembles stone or lava rather than wood. It has been wrought by the weather into shapes which no abstract sculptor could have imagined; only perhaps the men who carved the intricate groyning of the old cathedrals, with gargoyles and faces of demon-familiars leaning forth. Within a minute I had made out the head of a lion, the head of an owl, and the head of a bearded patriarch, side by side; and beyond them such mystical flowings of forms as might have been conceived by Blake in a vision.

I can prophesy two things about the Blind Cottages when their windows flash with new glass. One is, they will be renamed 'Three Ways' (they stand where they meet). The other is that the first thing a new owner will do will be to fell that enchanted oak. He will not have heard its lion roar, its owl hoot, nor its Prophet proclaim:

> 'He who kisses the Joy as it flies,
> Lives in Eternity's Sunrise.'

Though I may have kissed the Joy as it flies, must I buy this property and become a druid to preserve that oak?

'HE'S GONE,' she cried as if in glee. 'He's gone.'

Sometimes I would glimpse a busy trowel among the herbage, and I would know that the lady's hand would be grasping it. She was scrupulous and lived alone. Some time in Easter week she would be apt to reminisce of a cottage by the sea, and salty driftwood which had burned with green and blue flames. And—as if there were no connection—of a visitor she expected. Her gate, usually closed against livestock, would then be open, and a Jaguar stood before her house.

By nightfall or soon after the Jaguar would be gone, the gate shut and next day I could call with an offering of wild grasses or a windfallen bough, and take tea in her kitchen (everyone else had to sit in her parlour) because we both liked a stove with a hob. On the hob quince jelly would be simmering, while we talked gardens. But just occasionally a veil would be lifted for me as a trusted friend. I was told of those few occasions when it would not be convenient for me to call, and why.

So that, on a certain day I went my usual walk, and was careful to pass the lady's place like a stranger. I had never met this man who drove the Jaguar. Her daffodils stood stalwart and glad, just stirring their trumpets on erect stalks, being sheltered by a wall, in contrast to my own which at that moment were being thrashed by a gale on the verge of a pond.

Yet I had had the sheltered life: she had endured life's gale. She gave me to understand that she did not look forward to his periodic visits, since a day long ago when he had left her for another. Yet he could not forget her, nor she quite forget him. Her heart was one of war's casualties, and not unique. Henceforth love had been a Lenten vista with no hope of resurrection—unlike that of the Prince of humility the next Sunday. And yet, her passionate love of her garden, and those daffodils which appeared to generate a light of their own, stood for some inward resurrection to me.

She worked too hard in her garden, I told her; especially when the clock was put on in Easter week, as it was that year. She looked so very tired just before the visit. 'You overdo it,' I told her. But her spring garden had to be perfect, like her little house.

On the day of the Jaguar I took my usual walk, which was to a rural post-box, and afterwards a few minutes' meditation in a country church. I returned by the footpath that was more signposted than evident. A straying heifer also trod it and helped define it. A fallen bough lay under an oak. I shouldered it and marched on, knowing that she often needed to go 'sticking' since the days of the driftwood fire. She also made festival posies for the church, so on my way I plucked twigs of pussy-willow which was budding silver. The neatsfoot beast went before and kept turning round and glaring as much as to say, 'Why are you following me about?'

Only I knew the truth of her subsistence, and the pride of her independence. I laid my offering inside her gate when I came to it, knowing it would tell her that her well-wisher had passed by.

Earlier I had had a moment's glimpse past the Jaguar at her door of a stocky figure, presenting a prosperous

21

back, greeting her breezily with his hands on her shoulders. I averted my 'stranger's' gaze. On my return walk the Jaguar was gone: she stood on the gravel with a rake, raking out the marks of its tyres.

'He's gone!' she cried, as if in glee.

'So early? Where did he take you for lunch?'

'He had a business appointment on his way home: we had just a drink and a snack and a talk.'

'Your favourite ginger wine at the Woolsack?'

'No, sherry at some brash place opposite the service station. Do you suppose I'd take him to the chimney-corner of our conversations?'

'What did he talk about?'

'About his new boat and where he's going in it this summer. He left just in time for me to pick the flowers for my Easter posies.'

'In the rain?'

'I loved picking them in the rain. He smoked incessantly. The cottage reeks of smoke.'

'And he never asks how you are off for money?'

'It never occurs to him I'm living on a shoestring.'

'There now: and I was fondly imagining that you were nearing an understanding now that he's a widower, and had gone to have a jolly lunch and a bottle of wine.'

She shook her head. 'It wouldn't work. The cigarette smoke, for one thing ...'

'You half fear his coming, yet you don't forbid him. You greet him kindly when he comes.'

She drooped her head. 'The driftwood burned with beautiful colours once.'

'Didn't he ask you, now that at last he's free? I believe

22

he asked you to join him on the boat.'

She said nothing. I went on: 'Best forget him, then. It is a time for all new life, is Easter.'

'And so he expects a little forgiveness,' she said. She raised her face to her daffodils stirring like people preparing to dance. Her eyes suddenly reflected a gladness as single as theirs, as total as Easter after Lent.

I saw that her garden was the victory of her life.

❦　❦　❦　❦　❦　❦

TWO GLASSES of country wines, looking the April sun in the eye, were something to please us. The raspberries were trimmed and wired and greening into leaf here. Gooseberries, pruned, had branches clean and sharp.

Before us was a prospect of earth sprouting wheat and oats. If I were vicar of that little church on St. Michael's common, I should make wine of the wheat from the fields around it: I should bless it and offer it as a sacrament in that church whose cross is made of two hazel boughs cut from these hedges. To me who have witnessed the ploughing and the sowing and the harvesting, and have seen as it were this very cross hung with catkins, this would constitute a truth more valid than dogma.

Probably I should be severely censured by the Bishop for heretical practice, even though our God made the wheat as well as the vine. Why did the early Fathers make religion so difficult for us, fraught with personalities we cannot envisage nor understand? My D.D. cousin told me people were arguing the Godhead in every

23

barber's shop in Alexandria, so the Fathers had to make a ruling. Hence the Trinity of their imagining, apprehending or devising. But what can any ordinary person make of them, apart from the Holy Ghost being the air we breathe, which it is not, but in the Greek it is. Thus I was thinking in church the other Sunday, while confessing myself a miserable sinner, or rather a sinner not at all miserable, on account of April's sunlight and its birds singing outside.

I could more nearly imagine Pentecost from the sun-fire in our country garden wines. O happy light. We sat under a glass roof open to the south eating white cheese on brown bread, topped by discs of red beet. I am a dropper—of pennies, paper-clips, pencils. Today I dropped beetroot. A crimson slice slid off my cheese to the floor. The cat pounced: it looked as if murder had been done. Wrong prey. Red muzzle of white cat; red washed on to her whiskers by red paws. Another disc was laid on the Caerphilly on the bread: red, white, brown. Wine-gleams rocked across them. Hold steady now, in spite of rocking wine-gleams. Open mouth. Bite. Half the slice remained poised in my grasp. Happy biter; non-dropper. I praised again the tinctures of nature; how each thing selects from the rainbow to colour its sunshine.

All was bright out of doors: garden daffodil-studded, primrose-bordered. 'I must pick some,' she said, 'before that child comes again.' While his mother talked knitting patterns, she said, her jolly little Jack played leapfrog over the daffodil clumps. Crisp heads went snap.

'Hence that big round bowl of floral scrambled egg in your room?'

'Exactly.'

Else this would be Eden: the view no longer foggy nor skeletal, but diaphanous with swelling buds; the pond enlarged by winter's rains, a blue-and-white pane of sky.

'I dug a "grip" to drain the lawn. To the child it was a canal: he launched a nutshell boat. It floated backwards. The pond had begun draining itself back on to the lawn ...

' "Good-bye, Mrs. Tablet: you and your little Jack must come again ..." I rushed for a spade and dammed the "canal"; and for a basket for trumpet-picking. "O dem Golden Trumpets ..." Do you know that negro spiritual? No, I've just invented it. I love that child, but ... damn him, all the same.'

I told her, 'We had one visit us who played at wrestling with the garden hose. We watched helpless. "I think he'll be a designer," said a guest.

' "Or a sculptor; one of the new kind who create labyrinths of wire and call them DOOM or simply DEVICE."

'I dared to say, "I think he will be a snake un-charmer."

'Tommy's mother smiled appreciatively, then looked puzzled. She got up to go. "Come along, Darling."

'But Darling took some extricating; the snake had been winning.

' "You hold up that loop while I untwist this one. Take my hand, Darling, and balance on one leg a minute ... Can you get his left foot out...?"

'A Houdini with a provisional licence, I should say.'

We had a grandson, so intelligent: we tried to see our side of the family in those bright eyes. But when some ten minutes after his departure we found he had made a merry-go-round of the weights of the grandfather clock and the chains were tightly enmeshed, we were not so eager to take credit for the drive toward engineering experiment in that future genius. In fact, we also said, 'Damn the boy.'

Last month a granddaughter from Canada, never having been in England before, arrived with her mother after a flight of a day and a half, cold, hungry, in the dusk. Almost her first words were, 'Are there any graveyards around here? I want to see a graveyard.'

Surprising people, these buds of the 21st century. They certainly do tick—even the one who stopped the clock.

❧ ❧ ❧ ❧ ❧ ❧

'JOG ON, jog on the footpath way,' sang that rogue in Shakespeare. Jog is the word for it on our Suffolk clay, desperate for lack of frost and caked after an overplus of winter rain. The cloddy hardbake skitters under my boot-soles. Buried under the clods are kernels of corn. Nature pushes through a tender shoot somehow. A mushroom will lift two and a half tons, I'm told. Jog on.

The wind is hammering a piece of tin against a rusty building. Rust at a distance glows like sorrel. My first rose opened yesterday. Rust, too, can have flower colours. Here is a sea of nettles and long shining grass. Wind moans through crevices: 'ding-ding' sounds tin on tin. Over there I see a scarecrow which is waving one hand rhythmically as if by some mechanism. It is conducting the 'ding-ding' or seeming to. To me it is a ghost haunting the sunlight.

Places remain: people vanish. Daylight ghosts accompany us who keep step with memory. Glad ghosts, sad ghosts: 'ghosts of lovers dead and gone'—or just gone. Friends that were.

There is a cottage; that one with blind windows. Affectionate evenings of tea for two by a log fire are remembered there by Sighile. Enter a certain thatched inn. 'This is where he got his hair cut.' 'But it's an inn.' 'Yes, the barber used to call on Friday evenings. Customers sat enjoying a pint while waiting their turn.'

The sun shines outside: the young corn is glad and growing. 'Drink up.' A ghost still stirs a heart here, a daylight ghost.

I, too, meet ghosts; one on a particular cobbled street. I was yesterday sitting under a flowering cherry. I seemed to hear a voice: 'Come to Bath: the cherry trees are gay in their pink tutus'—something fanciful like that. But that friend is dead, aged 80, leaving a wardrobe stacked with creations by Worth, 1928. 'Do you mind?' she asked once, as I took her out to dinner. The effect was sensational: 1928 resurrected in 1962. Oh, she had an air. But I am sitting under a cherry tree in Bungay, and she and her elegances are vanished like smoke.

There is Henry (I say 'is') who could only tolerate the bud of Albertine, and could not tolerate Puccini at all. A highbrow? But a lover of old roses. His laugh was reverberate as heart of oak. He gave me my Gloire de Dijon: its first flower opened yesterday: 'Hallo, my Henry,' I say.

Have you not had a friend of whom, in a spring dawn or dusk, you still say, 'Oh, for an hour of his company again'?

Sometimes we say of a stranger, 'He reminds me of

27

Henry, or of Jim.' Henry improvising on his piano. Jim with his patent grill. 'We'd watch the morsels revolving on it while we had a sherry and chatted of corn and cows, and planned picnics.'

The cottage is now empty. And who now plays Henry's piano and where?

Thus thought-talking, I jogged along a headland of dry chapped earth. I came to a watercourse. I dangled down my feet in waterproof boots and landed on a patch of gravel. A shaggy perpendicular bank ten feet high faced me. I anchored my crook round a deep-rooted weed, gripped with the free hand a tussock of cocksfoot (and nettle). Heave-ho: a scramble and I was up. A brown carpet of rolled tilth was before me. Where was I? I saw a group of trees and a low red roof sitting among them like a hen on a nest.

Is that Sighile's place? I recognise her three hens peering at me through the hedge. I glimpse her rows of peas, beans and well-wired raspberry canes. I pass like a shadow along the outside of her hedge. I see her weaving baskets in her sun-porch. What is she thinking as her fingers weave cane? Has she ghosts to tea?

I, too, am in a peopled solitude, but a wayfaring solitude of vistas, images: that 'blow' of washing on her line for instance: sheets together, coloureds together, teacloths and towels together: secure, well-pegged. The antics of a line of washing fascinate me. I stay out of sight as audience of the ballet of hers. Her daffodils are over; their lamps are gone out. But her looks reflect the new summer light, and her cat is on her lap. I will not disturb her daydream, nor her ghosts.

My ghosts travel by daylight with the sweep of a

cloud's shadow; glad ghosts on the whole; yet they make spring wistful somehow. Perhaps hers are more household ones: the aura of a certain old table which I have seen her polishing with zest. She admits to enjoying her household chores. 'I am really a peasant at heart,' she has said.

I, too, am a peasant at heart: I prefer mould under my feet, and to cross a watercourse in my own way, sniffing wild mint and bruised sheep's parsley, and meeting a beetle eye to eye in the process. Peasants are fundamentalists, simple and psychic. They have never doubted ghosts nor angels.

I see Sighile rise and begin to take down her washing piece by piece, and fling each over her shoulder in a brisk wind-sweep of an action: sheets, garments, towels, till she has around her a toga of textiles scented with the country wind. Her line is now empty: the wind has only her hair to tease.

As she walks toward her door one small white square escapes and is blown over the hedge. I pick it up. It is a lace handkerchief, old, a little frayed, but of exquisite needlework. 'Hallo,' she says, suddenly aware of me as I hand it over. 'It was fleeing like a ghost,' I tell her.

'It was the gift of one who is now a ghost,' she says.

'Glad ghost?' 'Glad ghost,' she replies.

'This is one of mine,' I say, and sniff Henry's Gloire de Dijon lodged in my buttonhole of straw plait.

I roam onward and homeward. At the tin-dinging place the scarecrow is still waving its left hand.

MINSMERE, SUFFOLK: sea to the east, marsh to the west: the sea was very blue today. Motorists are warned of 'Bumps!' on entering the National Trust property. The road is humped at intervals to discourage speeding. Bumps are a test of mood. A driver has forgotten. Bump! Plump wife's bosom bounces: she is indignant. Bump! A youth and his girl laugh as their sports car bucks like a horse.

Middle-aged party spreads a picnic: the shaken woman still sulky. The young couple lift out a bottle of chianti, an Italian basket, a rainbow umbrella and saunter down to the marshy thicket. They submerge: they vanish totally, even the rainbow brolly.

Under a small birch with bright green heart-shaped leaves another young couple have spread their rug, near where I sit sketching. Of them, are now visible just two hands, hers with a ring with a small sparkle, and his.

'Are you asleep?' (I hear).

'M'm.'

'Shadows of leaves are dancing over your eyelids. Your eyelashes look like moths asleep.'

'Poet,' she murmurs. Her hand seeks for his as if fingers were antennae. They meet and entwine.

I sit here sketching the marsh view; rushes upstanding as a crop of wheat that is over-ripe, weathered. Beyond this a small wood of young conical trees, spring leaves golden-green, twinkling inwardly. Then a great sheet of shrill-green corn; then a wood of rounded trees; then silhouetted woodland, black, woolly-caterpillarish, creeping along the horizon.

Concentration tires the eyes. I turn aside. A middle-aged pair have come in view, trundling along the cliff-top. Suddenly they swing to each other and congeal in a powerful embrace, kiss with a bump, then kiss sostenuto. Ah. They separate, as if that had been a bumper of shared good wine; continue their colliding walk, his arm encircling her.

Bump! Bump! Another car-load touch the roof.

There is a murmur from under the birch-bower: 'It's the cherry I like, that soaked cherry ...'

Male voice: 'Why didn't you tell me? You could have had a martini there before. I saw you dancing in your mind to that "Skaters' Waltz"—the way your head moved to the muzak. I brought you to The Anchor because I know that Dick used to take you to the White Hart. I wanted there to be a place that's just us. The Anchor can be that.' No answer. 'Can't it?' Silence.

Then: 'Oh, Dick took you there too, did he? Is there any place around here where you've not been holding hands with Dick ... or somebody?'

'We were engaged.'

'With him it was martini with a cherry and "Where shall we dance?" With me, "bitter lemon" and "Is it too late to plant artichokes?"'

'Dick was well off.' Mumble-grumble. 'Oh, darling, I've told you ...'

'Artichokes,' he ejaculated, as if they were some sort of plague.

'It was I who broke it off, I prefer to marry you, my peasant poet.'

31

Ten minutes only had passed since it was: 'Your eyelashes look like moths asleep.' Never trust a poet, young
woman. I had dealt with the rushes that looked like a
crop of wheat overdue for the harvester. Now for the
twinkling coppice. I moved my pitch, wanting to sketch
the row of coastguard cottages while the light made
such sharp angles of shadow on their chimneys. Our
'poet' lay looking as if 'artichokes' were incised on his
heart. She sat bolt upright gazing at him with eyes of
tragic faithfulness.

The stout party's picnic was over. 'Now, for God's
sake, I don't want to be shaken to a jelly,' warned the
bosomy wife as she heaved herself into the car for the
return over the Bumps.

I, too, was thinking of packing up and strolled to my
car on the cliff-edge. At that moment the sporty couple
emerged from their hideout below and climbed to the
top. She was swinging the now-empty chianti flask as
if it were a joy-bell, and chattering of an adventure in a
wagon-lit by which, having shared her vacuum flask with
a stranger, the others concluded they were husband and
wife—'so they put us on the top pair of bunks'. The
drollness of the situation overcame her. 'Didn't sleep a
wink,' was her last decipherable utterance. Her sporty
boy friend, basket hooked on arm, hand gripping furled
rainbow brolly, supported her under an elbow with his
free hand and waited with a wan smile for her peals of
laughter to subside which sounded like the panic of some
marsh bird. He had the better head for chianti. He led
her to the coupé, packed her in beside him and set off at
a great pace. At every Bump the whole chassis leaped
into the air. She hiccupped and clutched herself.

The sun which spilt its rays in boundless gold all over our day was now compacted into a perfect sphere, an orange, sober and moon-meek. I called at The Anchor. Opposite me I found the pair who had exchanged that sudden cliff-top embrace, which had been bulky, ecstatic and prolonged.

Now I saw that he had provided most of the bulk, enclosing her like a tree its no-longer so-youthful dryad. He sat fondling her wrists with the reverence that a shivering man might bestow on the pipes of a radiator. His hands travelled almost to her elbows and back. He spoke in low tones. Her face was like one of the pre-Raphaelites' women, pale as Elaine, lit with a muted magic. She clasped his fingers as they returned from their trip to her elbows.

They rose at last and walked to the door. Then I saw that her legs did not match: one was shapely, the other shrunken, unnaturally thin. He pushed open the door with one arm: with the other he encircled her waist, swung her briefly off her feet and deposited her outside as carefully as if she were a china shepherdess.

Who is happy? I asked myself as I finished my beer.

※　※　※　※　※　※

A LARK alights in the lane in front of my bicycle, with his perky little crest: he pecks grit, then rises over the hedge, hovering as if a small electric current flowed through his wings: he tries a muted song, then sinks into the green corn. He is an event on a May morning to exorcise all the 'crucial issues' that play around our bemused brains like summer lightning. And that sudden little posy of pink clover on the grass verge—who would ever see it except he walked or moved slowly as I am doing, on two silent wheels—wheels which I cannot even see, for I have now this small-wheeled bicycle, and its front wheel is so small it is totally invisible from the saddle. I seem to be floating on air—which at moments unnerves me, like thinking about how you walk down stairs while you are doing it.

Now a butterfly with orange-tipped wings flutters out of the hedge and for fifty yards maintains exactly my speed a few feet ahead of me. Then he wavers into the hedge again. I become aware of multitudes of creatures in excited exploration of this hedge, birds so full of contrary impulses—to peck buds, to woo, to nest, to flick up water with their wings—that they can't stay on any one twig for more than a moment.

A rook now circles me: for some reason he regards me as of interest. Round and round he goes, with slow spasmodic wings, like slack black elastic, breasting the breeze, then slanting down it.

He's got bored with me: he's gone. Small birds have a way of flitting a few feet ahead of me from bush to bush. The light gives them a different tint the way it slips across them as they fly. A tit is blue, then yellow, then for a moment his back is like wet ink as he floats up to a branch. A chaffinch calls from one hedge, blackbirds and thrushes from the other. Or is that a nightingale—or a thrush imitating a nightingale? A nightingale is a prima donna thrush.

Pools of blue birdseye lie in the grass, backed by stitchwort, starry and dazzling. Another butterfly, pale blue,

34

swoops round me twice and is gone. Now a little old car, like a hurled parcel of black-and-rust, comes at a speed beyond control and on its wrong side and full of people, all laughing as I wince against the verge. It's like living in the time of the buzz-bombs: they hurtle into view, they pass, the hedgerow life resumes, and if you are lucky you are still alive too, and note again the vetches, the herb robert, the snow of petals lying under orchard trees, and the head-high lace of sheep's parsley flickering past.

There are more people in the fields than at any time of the year. A machine has not yet been invented to single sugar beet. Figures, straight or stooping, stand activating that sensitive antenna of the hoe, flicking and scraping. Mostly they are alone: several are in the view, but each on his acre. Elsewhere clouds of spray exude from machines, killing weeds and anaesthetising the breeze as it wafts this way. But bordering this by-way they can still be called wild flowers, unless some local authority condemn them also to be sacrificed to god-the-motor-car. The trees that have been felled to appease him don't bear thinking of.

A gap in the hedge reveals a rolling sea of green corn, rising over there into a froth of may-blossom and flower-ing chestnuts. I pass a field of oats whose broad blades and blue-green vigour speak of pigs. I know of old that hue of health. It is organic. I dare bet there are pigs on that farm. My brother-in-law kept 500 pigs. Yes, I know that colour of the corn.

As I approach the town the scent of the may conquers the smell of the sprays. Hedgerows give place to gardens. Then, in the town centre, the smell of diesel takes over, as Common-Market-size trucks straddle corners, mount pavements, and bully their way through medieval streets.

A seat at a crossways offers a welcome rest. I sit while traffic weaves around Queen Bess in effigy granting the town its charter. I remount, but stall in starting and fall off. This small-wheel bicycle has sensitive steering. I hope nobody saw me tumbling off my bicycle at nought m.p.h. One feels a fool falling off a bicycle for no reason.

Having bought the plants I came for, I flee the traffic, back to Queen Elizabeth, then abruptly get (not fall) off and walk the steep hill. In the country again, I am passed by a small boy. I pass him halted, gathering rabbit fodder. He rattles past me. He spots another patch of hogweed. I pass him. I have to stop and tie up my carrier, which my spill set rattling. He passes me. More hogweed ahead. I pass him. Goodbye, boy, I am turning right. My eyes are level with a church tower poking out of treetops. I don't have to pedal again till I am passing the lychgate, only inhale the breeze of my glide.

While walking uphill through the suburb I observed a back of a minibus and someone climbing into the driver's seat. I saw just an elegant leg glimmering through black nylons, and a neat black shoe. As I came abreast I saw a young nun sitting at the wheel. Another young nun sat beside her. They were chattering vivaciously. As I walked ahead I still heard the young voices. How wonderful, I thought, to be so bubbling over on this May morning, in a life vowed to celibacy and selflessness. The shortened skirts of nuns' habits diminish their otherworldliness, even to revealing, willy-nilly, on one getting into a car, an elegant leg clad in elegant hose, since the cheapest hose today is not-unglamorous nylon. Part of this May morning, along with its thrushes and finches, will always be for me that religious leg.

※　　※　　※　　※　　※　　※

A SMALL group of bow-topped wagons was gathered on the vase expanse of Bungay Common. Horses grazed, the wind ruffled their manes, the gorse bloomed, the hames shone, and the little flowers of fantasy that adorned every wagon's every cupboard, batten, and turned spindle looked as freshly varnished as the wildflowers of the verges, where buttercups now proclaim that freedom is golden if you travel at three miles an hour.

'No, we shall not be home tonight,' said a wagon-wife. If your house is arched over your back, the horizon can wait till tomorrow.

After tea, at a quiet word or two, steps were removed and stowed, shafts lifted, horses backed, traces secured. Then, in the right traditional way, with an oblique start, something less than half-lock of the front wheels, which eases the dead pull of starting straight ahead, they moved off in procession.

I sheltered in my car against a sharp shower, its nose close to a dull grey fence. I watched the bow-tops go over the bridge: all that neatness, adornment, homeliness, just a skin removed from wind and wet, as warm and mortal as the body of a man. The grey plank fence was all my view now. Then I saw that a straggle of pretty leaves had pushed through a crack and was waving to the wind on the heath. I sat there a long time looking at that fence and at the green leaves struggling through it: rain

37

sparkled on the windows. I thought of Huntingfield's church restored to its original colours, whose roof also looks gipsy-ish. Gipsies give their children Biblical names or fairy-tale ones: a Shadrack married a Cinderella. Before 'good taste', art was as exuberant as Maytime.

A 'traveller' is different in his inner man from a house-dweller. He belongs to Genesis. But aren't we all nomads? Our days are wheels under us. Tomorrow is a new place.

Jog on. Slide into a ditch, climb out of it. Think one thing today, another thing tomorrow. Goodbye yester-day: 'Ae fond kiss and then we sever.' Welcome, young bramble leaves escaping through the fence. I think you have the secret of today. I think I am a bow-topped wagon with a sky-blue ceiling. Gee, then, but as slowly as ever foot can fall: let buttercups pass in golden sheen.

What makes me want to stare at this dull grey fence so long, and its escaping green bramble? Life is a love affair or it is a prison. A sandwich in the pocket is freedom. Jog on. Look at that crazy jumble of old sheds which I sat and sketched where I ate my sandwich. Are they not lovely, my scrawled black hovels of wood, old iron and swamp-blacked roofs, the whole lot wading in nettles?

To contemplate the rickety conglomeration is to love it and its doors drooping from single hinges. I have installed in it some of my best ghosts, even as Sighile still houses a glad ghost in a certain sad empty cottage. Today she feeds brown hens in a paddock which is 'paradise enow'. I lounge under two cherry trees in Bungay and pretend to be idle.

HERE WAS I on a day reputedly hot, sitting on a table tomb. Cool tomb sending a delicious chill up my spine while I sketched headstones that looked to be on their way to the door in the wall. There were three abreast in front, followed by two with pretty nicks in their sloping shoulders. Curious how alive old headstones look as you sketch them: their arrangement has a 'going somewhere' look.

I wondered who lived behind the door in the wall, between the lilac and the japonica. Once a nun would have done, I suppose. Empty arches of a 13th-century convent stood around, sprouting wallflowers. The door opened. Inside was a tiny garden; a small pool with a small fountain playing, a stone cat on the brink, and two white chairs like iron foliage. Most traders forsake their shops at six and go home to bungaloid outskirts with glossy-magazine kinds of gardens. But Gabriella, I see, lives above her gown shop. And was this Gabriella looking out from the doorway? She was expecting somebody: on a table stood two tall glasses of some cooling drink.

Here comes the visitor, stepping nimbly through one of the time-nibbled arches. Twenty minutes later, the door reopens. She presses his hand: he takes a quick look round, which misses my crouching figure, gives her a swift kiss. The door closes again. My eyes dazzle over sunlit white paper: the daisies seem to have turned pink. I stroll round into the market place. It is market

39

day. A handsome young Hebrew displays cloth under his stretched hands.

Gabriella's gown shop stands beside a garden shop whose window offers what look like baths for crumpled old men: they are 'garden pools'. I am glad that Gabriella's pool is round. She is now in her shop, I see, doing accounts at a corner desk. A salesgirl consults her, garment on arm. I was to meet my wife in the shop, who was searching for a summer frock, something for 'every day' she stipulated as I entered. Would not a 'has-been best' do for every day, so she could buy a new 'best' instead, I queried? No, she said, a past best frock won't do any more than city clothes would do in the country. 'But my father climbed cliffs in city clothes,' I said, 'his watch chain swinging against his black waistcoat.'

'Your father was a very unusual man.'

Women always seem to be looking for something which ... and there definition ends.

In the gown room a young man stood looking out of the window, while behind a carelessly drawn curtain a vigorous bare arm flickered. A hand opened the curtain and a girl stepped out and stood looking at her man with a tentative smile, a ticket on the back zip. The young man obviously had ideas: he surveyed the effect. 'It's not quite ...' 'No, not quite ... is it?' she agreed.

I watched the salesgirl agonising to understand what they did want; something exacting but vague; a garden frock ... but not a garden party frock, nor yet a frock for gardening in ... but something sort of ...

The row of limp gowns, like ghosts in a queue, stirred faintly as a hand dived in, as with hopes of bodies to accommodate with love, or something in lieu of love;

admiration or self-esteem. I have known women who still love men who don't even notice when they are wearing a new gown. But for these two, the buying of a dress was more like a conspiracy.

Meanwhile my wife found what she liked but it was too large or too small. 'You are a difficult size, madam.' We smiled to hear this yet again. It never occurred to me when I courted her that she was a difficult size; she seemed a very nice size indeed.

'A sweet disorder in the dress ...' the young man quoted as his donna emerged yet again from yet another robust struggle of white arm and shoulder behind the casual curtain. 'But it has a flowing line,' the salesgirl protested, thinking she was contradicting him.

Outside, the market stalls were a flourish of hands picking and choosing, paying, receiving. On the opposite pavement a man prowled slowly to and fro, some twenty yards one way and back again. He was neatly bearded, too neatly for the current Englishman, I thought. He suggested some French professor from a Lycée. He strode with slow, dogged tread as if obsessed with missing the lines between the paving stones. His hands behind his back played an invisible piano.

A tortoise-faced man followed his wife round and round the stalls. He stooped slightly forward as if being jerked by a lead which she held in her hand. Neither exchanged a word. She prodded the air with her nose a few yards from each stall.

'More of a ...' began the lass of lively vigour, stirring again the gowns on the rail.

At that moment a procession of four gipsy caravans came by, with clatter of hooves and nodding horses' heads. Gentlemen gipsies, they looked.

The French professor's hands ceased suddenly their sonata. The tortoise-man stopped and blinked. His leash seemed to have snapped. His wife was already at a distance. They jerked about for each other in a panic. Madam Gabriella raised her pen and gazed wistfully out of the window. Stallholders waved their gay stuffs with greater abandon to counter the attraction of the caravans. The salesgirl had a sudden inspiration. 'You mean—something gipsyish?'

The ghostly queue was fluttered yet again. Within minutes emerged from the curtain a green gown incarnate: it had a frolicsome pattern, controlled, but only just, by vertical bands of plain colour.

'That's it!' he exclaimed. 'That's "Down by the salley gardens my love and I did meet": yes, that's it.'

The caravans passed on their way. Market day resumed.

'I will wear it now,' she said, and the ticket was removed from the 'down by the salley gardens' gown. And later I spotted the pair of them beside the river. Sheep's parsley was falling across their faces; and there was a 'sweet disorder' in her dress, the long dress which the salesgirl was inspired to call 'gipsyish'.

❋　❋　❋　❋　❋　❋

AFTER THE broadcasting of Parliament—noises that sounded like the Mad Hatter's tea party—no wonder I find myself looking for an alternative society. O babe, vociferating to heaven, I am with you. Infant of a few weeks, looking like Moses in a rush basket, lifted into father's arms, then yielded to a lady in a green gown by force of her devoted look, a lady whose children are grown up.

You can tell a natural mother: see how her arms take the body of the babe, how her hands place themselves. My own mother forgot how to hold a baby, was helpless with my own. This lady's hands were expert still: she seated herself so that the infant faced a leafy shade. I prefer children who can feed and dress themselves; but I had to reverence her for her reverence of the babe. Neither of the two now uttered: it was an adoration; how mystic, I alone perceived.

As a farmer I have watched many a new-born beast groping blindly yet surely for the source of warmth and sustenance. It looked to me like a sort of magic, the knowing without knowing.

Near by was a wall of cardboard. Infant of a week cries, 'Help! Food! Comfort!' Within three years the creature hath a purpose and its eyes are bright with it— to paint a mural on this cardboard wall: no matter if its hair gets coloured green and yellow in the process.
And after...? 'My life begins when my job ends,' said a man who welded bumpers on to cars all day. Said a fellow worker, 'I recite Gray's Elegy to myself. But I don't have Jim's output.'

Market stalls attract strollers: babes attract mothers. 'Look at the tiny toes, all perfect.' Dames become suddenly as damsels one year wed. The lady in the green gown relinquished the babe and returned to her piccage. This was a craft market among the hillocks of Bungay Castle, along with country dancing to pipe and tabor.

43

Participation is the word. I stand less steadily than once I did, convalescing not from illness but from life itself. I have an illusion I could dance those romping roundelays. 'You'll fall on your face.' There is a youth prisoned in these bones that would dance to pipe and tabor.

'Come and entertain us,' the village W.I. asked the Arts Trust. There was an entertainment of grace and wit by four dancers, miming and dancing every dance I had danced in my youth. Most evocative was a solo saunter; a body's musing to the tune of 'Summertime'. Don't we all do that; saunter about our room, hum, cut a few quiet capers, lie down, get up, toe the intricacies of the pattern of the carpet in a sort of hop-Axminster game? Or don't you ever do that? 'Stop,' I say to myself. 'Think who you are.' I ask my image in the mirror, 'Who the deuce are you?'

The other day I saw a new horse-drawn caravan in the forecourt of a house, built on the premises. Diamonds of rain were dancing off every cornice: red, green, golden. Even its wheels were gay, would revolve like catherine wheels behind a smartish horse. Afterwards in Dunwich Forest I stood looking along a corridor of fir trunks, like a log-cabin trains-long, to a narrow threshold of verdant light. Better than a dream, that day of the caravan of exuberant wheels. I sometimes think the only way to escape the dominance of 'things' is to live in a caravan. Else, 'things' multiply and encrust one's life like barnacles a ship's bottom. There is also this numbers game run by the Bank, which tells me quite arbitrarily if I am rich or poor. Sometimes I think I am rich when I am poor and vice versa.

I asked the green gowned lady on her 'piccage' (or rug)

called 'Gardencraft', 'What sells best?' 'Rosebuds and mint today,' she said. A small girl lifted up a Gardencraft puppet and embraced it; even as the green-gowned lady took into her arms the weeks-old babe. It was a monk puppet. Child would not be parted from her monk. Father put hand in pocket; it was sold.

Awaiting the dancers the other evening outside the village hall, I sketched a tree. If I can't dance, my pencil can; it does nimble hops and skips (that's foliage), swoops and tangoes; that's trunks and boughs. In the entertainment I admired a fierce and swirling waltz danced by a man with a lay figure for partner. I saw in that figure all the girls I partnered in my twenties; pink face, fair fluff of hair, speechless. Speechlessly we whirled. Speechlessly sat out; I urgently romantic, she monosyllabic. I got nowhere—until I met Annabel. Then—liberation, but briefly.

   🎕   🎕   🎕   🎖   🎖   🎖

I COULD have been a Tennyson, I tell myself, if only rhymes had not got in the way. Rarely would the right sensible rhyme turn up to complete a couplet.

It was curious, then, that my first poem, a sonnet I wrote to my girl at the age of 20, came as easily as shelling peas. I was ploughing. Nothing so conduced to beautiful thoughts or no thoughts at all as to be guiding a Suffolk swing plough behind two good horses. Not so much guiding as just feeling 'bottom' with it: the horses did all that was needed, if it was set right as to 'foot' and 'hake'.

What a lovely morning that was; yet my sonnet was all about darkness and death. A premonition? No, just a Keatsian gloom most typical of youth in love. Annabel lived in Bury St. Edmunds, some 12 miles away. But I wanted her in my arms, in my cottage farmhouse. All winter our longing grew. By the time the white and red may bloomed again, we could stand it no longer. In a mad moment Annabel told her family she was invited to spend a weekend in Long Melford at her friend Nancy's home. Nancy also had a boy who ached for her: she was readily sworn to the deception. On a Friday afternoon Annabel set out on her bike as if for Melford, but arrived at my cottage near Stradishall at tea time. She saw me unhitching Boxer and Kitty, and set about getting tea. I baited my pair, and we took our tea into the Pightle (a paddock). Later I turned the horses out to pasture and returned to the paddock. We were there till supper time—and after, watching a fine-weather afterglow.

For nearly three days we two lived the life that was planned for Adam and Eve. As for a forbidden tree of knowledge, perish the thought as far as we were concerned: we were much too preoccupied with each other. If 'knowledge' were forbidden, so much the better, since ignorance was bliss. Were our progenitors all that much in love, I have wondered, that they could so soon be looking for a diversion?

Gone was all my Tennysonian 'moaning of the bar'. All now was jolly Herrick. The breeze hissed through the small leaves of an elm above us. The tall grass was as a stockade, frail yet strong as faith. The rich herbage would have been a feast for any botanist; but we were not there to botanise. It suddenly occurred to me, and I told Annabel that these flowering grasses, the chaliced buttercups, the marguerites with petals white as skirts awhirl, were doing just what we were doing. Life never seemed more simple and honest than at that moment. Of a book of those days which I wrote later, a paper commented on 'Adrian Bell's exasperating reticence'. I had a proper shyness of our sacred bond, our green bond of wind-ruffled grasses. Cocksfoot and Timothy, foxtail and rye-grass bowed their flowery heads to us, nodded, 'Yes, yes.' What a 21st birthday present was Annabel. Looking back through half a century, those days still spell liberation. Any youth who has been under a possessive mother's suspicion of even a waft of feminine scent on his clothes will understand.

And time was pressing. My mother was no longer able to endure her marriage without the companionship of her eldest son. She wrote to tell me she was planning to come out to me to 'look after me', bringing with her my small brother and sister, leaving my father to fend for himself in London. Already their good family home in Enfield was being offered for sale. I must speedily transform our brief game of husband-and-wife here into reality and so seal my right to a home of my own.

Annabel and I spent half Saturday and all Sunday in that corner of the paddock, uttering little more than that monosyllable which is said to make the world go round. Hens' beaks appeared now and then through the cocks-foot: 'What's all this? Cluck-cluck.' It was an idyll also of an old-fashioned cottage range. Annabel cooked me lovely breakfasts. She lay on a bank on Saturday morning watching me at plough, or dozing: we were a bit short of sleep. Only the vicar called. 'Ah,' I cried, bustling Annabel into my little dairy. 'I was just in the middle of churning.' 'I won't keep you then,' he said, and soon departed.

Annabel and I said goodbye at midday on Monday. 'Let it be soon,' I urged, meaning marriage, having just received another letter from my mother, enthusiastic for life on the farm. Annabel nodded vehemently with that little pout of her lower lip expressive of desire.

'I can't live without you,' I declared.

I took her bag and strapped it on her carrier, while she lingered behind, taking a last look at the low-beamed room which had been our 'married' home of three days. As her cycle rounded a bend in the lane she looked back and waved. I returned to my plough. When I came home to tea and went into the house I found on the table a leaf of that sweetbriar whose scent, as we sat in the porch, had made us even more avid for each other. On the leaf was inscribed in black ink I C L W Y.

A fortnight later Annabel really did pay her friend Nancy a visit to ask her to be her bridesmaid. The tragedy that ensued lived long in her friends' minds in Melford. She looked back and waved to Nancy on pedalling away, as she had done to me. Her cycle swerved and a following car hit it; she was killed instantly.

When the news reached me I had just deciphered the meaning of I C L W Y on the rose leaf. Alas, I had to, after all, Annabel.

My mother descended on me, with furniture, family and maid. Not for another ten years did I escape that mixture of charm and pique by which she enslaved me, not until I met and married my present dear wife in 1931.

'Sumpin's bin lyin' here and spoilt a fair bit o'hay,' said my man Fred when we mowed the paddock. I had no words—none at all.

※　　※　　※　　※　　※　　※

JENNY THE Guernsey cow was in her chalet: her new calf lay beside her, of a silvery roan. Fresh wheat straw was under them, not concrete. So we bedded our stock in former days—on straw, always straw, lots of straw. Ethel was bringing out tea.

I had been sketching by the roadside, attempting the lovely grass. Sighile came gliding by on her bicycle. 'You do set yourself some difficult subjects,' she said kindly, then, 'I'm going to Ethel's to tea.'

'Do you know the short cut through the orchards?'

'That would be trespassing.'

'I have permission, if you don't mind walking your bike.'

I led the way to the pylon. 'Under or round? If it's bad luck to walk under a ladder, what will a pylon do to you?' I walked under, Sighile round. Then up a private lane of elms and dog-roses. 'There you are.' I pointed to Ethel's cottage and stopped. But Ethel was at her gate and beckoned me in. Who could say no to tea in Ethel's garden?

We sat on a little lawn under a big sun-brella. Before us were sweet williams, candytuft, bushes of old-fashioned roses; great mounds of Rosa Mundi with its striped pink and scarlet blooms. On the tea tray was a white cloth hand-embroidered with small flowers.

Then Ellmore appeared in a flashing white shirt carrying a linen prop he had just cut from a coppice for Sighile. The white insides of the cups flashed too, were dazzling till they filled with tea from the pretty green teapot. I wore green as I always do, and Sighile wore polka dots on white, and we were all green and white under the big umbrella.

I was at ease with these teacups. Drawing-room teacups frighten me, tapering to small bases: they slide about as if the saucers were greased. But these cups were graceful yet firmly founded: also there were cucumber sandwiches and layer cake: and what I might drop did not matter. There was a dog who licked up any crumb as if it had not been.

Broad beans in bloom, the sweet breath of cow, scent of fresh wheat straw came in wafts as in the days when field beans scented whole landscapes, and our cow-yards and horse-yards were deep in the straw of our tall wheats like Little Joss, our stout wheats like Squarehead's Master. Ellmore and I talked of days when we had milked and foddered together, and we had walked the land all day. We did a lot of walking then; 12 miles a day horse-hoeing. You didn't seem to feel the foot-slogging: there was quiet: you could talk as you went: there was a nice firm tilth. Then we looked at Jenny, cured of her milk fever.

'Didn't Strawberry have milk fever?' 'No, that was Buttercup.' Strawberry, mother of the herd, was a wonder cow, with a huge belly and bag, always a fillpail, always in good health. She walked last as by right when I fetched up the herd. I laid my hand on her back as we walked, slowly, slowly; a neatsfoot promenade. What was there to think about? Cows and crops: the future herd, next year's cropping. And always my hand on Strawberry's rump rocking with the rhythm of her hindquarters. The hand remembers—a girl's waist, Strawberry's backbone under the twitching hide, frosted mangold leaves in winter dawns, the feel of a handful of hay when it was just not too rare to cart, you judged. The hand remembers.

Ours was the cottage garden talk of retired husbandmen. But how say 'retired'? We each of us here had about an acre of ground to tend.

'Something ate my peas or they rotted,' said Sighile.

'Jenny strayed and ate my onions.'

'My lettuces want a nice rain.'

'Moles play the devil under my broccoli plants.'

'What animal will keep my grass down?' asks Sighile. 'Geese? I bespoke some goslings.'

'Then look out when there's a thunderstorm. You'll find them all on their backs, dead.' I did a mime of a gosling dead on its back, as far as a human could. 'You'll have to run out and bring them in and lay them on the hob. They'll revive. Early October they get airborne and fly away. Ours did.'

'What else is there? Sheep?'

'Sheep get the foot-rot, the fly-blow.'

She shuddered at the foot-rot. 'Or goats?'

'Goats will eat anything *but* grass: lace curtains on gooseberry bushes, even the flowers off a hearse—my friend's did.'

Sighile said, 'I had a pig once: it became too fat to get out of the sty. It had to be hoisted out by a crane.'

'Pigs on grass act as ploughs if they aren't rung.'

51

'How do you ring a pig?'

'One stands astride it and grips both ears, while the other with a sort of pincers ...'

'Ugh!'

What beast is a substitute for the lawn-mower which is killing us all as we grow older and still chase it? That is the 64-dollar question every one of my friends is asking.

Another tour of the roses, whose names ring down the ages: Rosa Mundi, Roserie de l'Hay, Maiden's Blush.

'A scythe.' Ellmore at my age has been scything grass for hay for Jenny. 'The scythe, it's a knack: it's all in the honing and the swing.' We looked at one another; so simple a tool, yet so subtle. It was once half of the rhythm of rural life; and the other half those romping folk dances, exhausting to us who are always creeping to the surgery for pills. I recalled at that moment the tide of tall grasses in All Saints' churchyard, the gravestones like submerged rocks: a church wading in hay, 'redundant', silent, lonely; yet the altar vessels shining, as in a legend. Shall I ever forget all that waist-high grass nodding to the summer day? And a double headstone, carved as if it were two, yet of one piece, to Pattie and John; so death did not them part.

※　　※　　※　　※　　※　　※

WE WALKED homeward from Ethel's through the orchards, Sighile pushing her bike, while I carried the linen prop Ellmore had cut for her, a noble shaft of ash. When we reached the tarmac lane she mounted and departed with that agreeable whirr of a cycle in perfect order. I turned the opposite way, to store her prop until it could be transported. I thought of my own cycle, by no means silent; a 'bump, bonk, ding' thing that rings its own bell at every pot-hole.

I reached home to find my wife just returned from taking a cousin to Heveningham Hall; a sort of Buckingham Palace set down on a field, to whose grandeurs I am peculiarly immune. I prefer the peas and sweet peas, the roses and broccoli, of a cottage garden on a summer afternoon, including Jenny the cow and her calf, whose bedding is composted to fertilise that plot.

Why Blake should want to go and build Jerusalem in England's green and pleasant land, beats me. A sort of Heveningham Hall, I suppose. The blatant gemmery of the New Jerusalem turns me to stone: 'of pure gold like unto clear glass ... The first foundation was jasper; the second sapphire, the third a chalcedony ... emerald ... sardonyx ... jacinth ...' Very wonderful, Your Divine Majesty; but a mud hut if you please for me and my gal, if it's a choice, or a willow cabin beside one of those tiny Suffolk streams; the Chet or the Box, or the stripling Stour at Sturmer. Yes, please God, and no possessions. So long as love is for a lintel, and gladness of love for a window, and faith in love for a latch, secure in which waking and sleeping should be mutually enfolding. Amen.

What need have I of palaces open to the public, when I can have Prospero's 'insubstantial pageant' in view most evenings just the thither side of a certain oak tree? For weeks I have seen a golden glow across about fifty thousand blackcurrant bushes in a flat field. I coveted the view

53

beyond them, where the landscape warps into slopes of corn in ear, stirring under the evening sky.

BUMP, BONK, ding! I have arrived on my old iron. Unload the linen prop which shall lift Sighile's sheets into the wind, where they make a noise like galloping. 'Sit, Jessica ...' Shakespeare understood all this. We are in sight of the promised land, even that glory of the sunset beyond fifty thousand blackcurrant bushes. This by location is Sighile's treasure, which cannot be bought or sold; an afterglow across a prospect dipping to the 'Blind Cottages' and rising to Manor Farm.

'Sit, Jessica ... on such a night ...' Sit, my lady, observe that wondrous sky. For some people happiness is always somewhere else; for me only just beyond a flatness of fifty thousand blackcurrant bushes. Sit at the foot of this oak and inherit the view. Flecks of splendour peep through a pink and dappled sky. There is a vapour trail where a plane zoomed high: it stands fretted like a great white lupin among spilled rose petals. Sit, Jessica ... Shakespeare knew the bliss of quiet gazing. Sit, just let it all happen. What is life to tangle us so? People house ghosts of lost affections in their eyes, which tint with nostalgia present associations. A man I knew was mentally ill for months because he moved house at seventy. A ghost is always in the light between thee and me in a world which lives on its nerves, instead of peasant-fashion in its customs of seed-time and harvest.

'Sit, Jessica. Look how the floor of heaven/Is thick

54

inlaid with patines of bright gold.' The first star is already trembling in the zenith. How easy it was to sit upon the ground when one was young: no creaks, no cramps. Ah, happy state when once I lay with my head on my girl's lap in the orchard of my little farm, and stared at such a sky. We were one, in brief halcyons of the teacup storms of first love between missing dates, and being forgiven; or being kept waiting till one felt oneself deserted, and forgiving ('I met a friend who would not let me go'). 'Jessica' is long in her grave; but I who loiter here in another sunset am the more touched by the innocence of our vows of 'each-otherness', as we called it. There is no shadow now between us: I see right through her: she is that sky, and she is me. We gather wraiths as we go, which become in some way ourselves.

I have been lying in the lap of mother earth. Stars begin to wink. Country housewives have been gathering their soft fruit all day. One now puts her head round the oak tree where I lie beside earing barley. 'Are you still alive? Still staring at the sky?'

'Yes, and assuaged of my craving for that realm of the setting sun over toward Manor Farm, which is all yours for a glance any clear evening. But I'm as stiff as your linen prop: please help me up. Thanks. Where did I leave my bike?'

'Here. Can you mount?'

'Yes.' I mount.

'Are you safe?'

'No. Is life? If I fall and break my neck, I'll give you a ring from some other world to tell you. Fate cannot harm me: I have for a talisman that "insubstantial pageant" viewed from your oak tree, which shall light

55

me past fifty thousand blackcurrant bushes. Fare you well.'

Bump, bonk, ding! I am on my way.

※ ※ ※ ※ ※ ※

FOR THE sake of saving five pounds of our garden peas from going to waste we bought a freezer for some eighty pounds sterling. It may sound extravagant. Considering it in the dawn of another day, I thought it a reasonable transaction, since new peas are real and rare, whereas eighty pound notes are in themselves nothing—or, if anything, about twopennyworth of processed wood pulp.

Since then, things have been piling into that magic cabinet. Even rhubarb, which after spring hitherto ran riot, has suddenly found itself plucked, chopped, and put in this intensive care unit, much to its surprise. Our appetite now whetted for freezer fodder, we went with Sighile pea-gleaning in the wake of the viner on her neighbour's field. At least, the two gleaned, while I gazed at that vale of green and harvest hues which my eyes always covet in this sunset hour.

I dropped a pod into a basket in a conversational way, as I revelled in the new angle of the fruitful vista which this high field presented. It was like a page of the Psalms, it really was; so that I sang inwardly, then dropped two or even three pods at a time, in thankfulness that we were here with hands to gather what otherwise would have been wasted, since the viner cannot get quite as close to the verge as the seed drill could.

'What house is that?' I interrupted Sighile to ask. She

told me I knew it well but was seeing the back of it. Once more I asked myself, 'Why go abroad?' This new vista was 'aboard'. When every pail, basket and bag was filled, we crept in low gear bouncily along the cart track, flanked by wheat as straight and solid as a block of gold in this breathless dusk.

Next day was pea-popping day. We worked automatically and fast at this, sitting in our vine-house under swelling bunches of grapes. Sighile would be under her vine on her veranda popping pods also. Thus we squirrelise as August comes in and winter seems again possible. The pop of the pod and the ding of the peas in the basin were mesmeric. Surely Adam and Eve must have been thus blissfully vacant after labouring and loving in the arbours of Eden, before that fatal fruit.

They weren't so much sinners as fools to my view. It would have taken more than Satan dressed up as a snake to tempt me and my gal to pluck knowledge and lose magic. Early in life I was forewarned by that story, which I took literally. I put up a resistance to being educated, which was largely successful, with the result that the freezer for which I sat popping peas, and Sighile's 'fairy ring' in which I wished last year and was granted my wish could be equally magical. To say that a certain fungus breeds in a perfect and expanding circle explains nothing to me. It looks like a lot of little people under brown umbrellas getting set for a rain dance.

Meanwhile our vegetable garden is raving with fertility. Dwarf beans are imagining themselves mauve-flowering runners, while runner beans have outstripped the 8-foot rustic poles I cut with my bill-hook, and are trying to climb each other and reaching for the sky. And we have to stake every Brussels-sprout plant.

As for the marrows, with their great gaudy blooms, how their five-pointed yellow trumpets must have gladdened the Garden of Eden. How do we know that vegetable life has no ecstasies and agonies? Each marrow flower has in its centre a clutch of what look like tiny golden eggs. I suppose they are stigmas or stamens or some name in Latin, and have to do with the plant's sex. Latin names drain the fun and the fear out of things: they make life sound like a laboratory. Until you enquire of Ovid, that is. Then, as Joe Gargery said in a different context, 'What larks!'

So much for plant life; but as soon as you find yourself born a human being you are taught that Adam and Eve were ashamed of being seen naked. A policeman, if present, would have flung his cape round the lady, even while the Lord of All was telling the blazing trumpets of the gourds, 'Blow me an Olympian diapason: enjoy yourselves hugely: your lusty unknowingness is more blest than the itch to Know of this naughty boy and girl who are now afraid of being seen with nothing on. I tell them there will come a time, to be labelled "Victorian", when even table legs will seem indecent to them. Out of the Garden with you, you two who can't appreciate even the love life of a courgette.'

With such high thoughts I gazed at our first marrow flowers, each guarding its clutch of tiny golden 'eggs'. Praise the Lord, O my soul, and don't forget that the most revered of the Saints had a high old time in their youth, before they founded celibate orders to keep boy and girl apart—Francis of Assisi not excepted. As for

58

St. Augustine, I've always thought it rather mean of him to abandon the loving mistress who had followed him and been faithful to him, and to whom, since she bore him a beloved son, he once might have exclaimed, 'With my body I thee worship,' which noble line the Church has shamefacedly scanted in its marriage service.

'Not for our sins, but for our blunders, O Lord, forgive us.' My mother never tired of quoting this to me. Who with certainty shall define a sin? But we know our blunders and have blushed for them.

❀ ❀ ❀ ❃ ❃ ❃

STICK AN 'e' on to 'fair' and what do you get? As motley a thing as England today. What price being a peasant? Would one be allowed to be so wantless? 'Onion soup and bread' was offered in Barsham Glebe by a loving young couple sitting between a big black pot and a small tent.

Barsham Faire, to which we were bidden to come 'gaudily garlanded', had the local Press checking their Piers Plowman, and me checking my Chaucer. We bypass Defoe, who noted in 1724 that Stourbridge Fair (no 'e') was like a canvas London on a stubble field, doing hundreds of thousands of pounds' worth of trade, of which the 'filth' left behind, trodden in and ploughed in amply repaid farmers for occupation of the site and compression of the soil.

The emphasis at Barsham Faire today was Organic: 'Organic Carrots'. Booths were walled with green bracken, one with flowers. The bread with the 'onion soup' looked densely organic. But what would our farmer say of 'organic' refuse left on the Barsham Glebe as compensation for record attendance figures for a three-day occupation? Somehow 'organic' came more naturally once.

Stourbridge Fair was a serious business. Only on the last day were races run, to entertain 'the meaner sort'. But Bury St. Edmunds Fair was a gay occasion, where the nubile gentlewomen of three counties were said to assemble to offer themselves to the highest bidder (which Defoe dutifully protests was a scandalous allegation).

Faire or no faire, we are very organic up our lane here. We have the peasant ideal. My neighbour Sighile had provided a little seat for me beside her on her fair-ground rug (or 'piccage') in a neat bay of blackberry bushes. Hereon she displayed her handiwork: woven floral chaplets and bracelets, wholemeal bread and scones, a bowl of passion flowers, baskets of posies—all of her own weaving and growing and baking. She has green fingers, and fingers strong to knead and weave, subtle to adorn.

My wife says she saw one medieval lady riding something on the Barsham road: it could only have been a bicycle: it was invisible under her gown. There was a small boy, hobby-horse to the maypole dancers, who was simply a golden head and a swirl of green damask, bounding with wondrous rhythm. I saw about fifty Kate Greenaway girls come dancing out of a green dragon's mouth to revolve the ribands of the maypole. Also folk dancers, 'properly habited' as Shakespeare would have said, and gaitered with chimes. I seemed to recognise Chaucer's pilgrims: Wife of Bath (several Wives of

Bath), plump friars by nature tonsured. Madame Eglentyne, the 'Nonne', I saw handing across a pound note in some game of chance. As for carls, churls, villeins—how genuinely easy to be one of those by donning sackcloth as the farm men of my generation did when gateways let tumbrils in up to the axles, when carting off roots in November, and every horse's hoof spurted a mud fountain, four of them in rhythm. Plenty of villeins here in Sunday-best sackcloth.

Little girls adorned themselves with my friend's chaplets and bracelets. Her last two scones I sold in her temporary absence to a young boy 'for Mum and Dad'— and got the change right. Passion flowers sold, posies sold. We had a view of blue smoke from a great grill accommodating half-trees, on which sizzled chickens' legs to a near-by folk rhythm as if they had danced off their chickens. By midday was a general gnawing of chickens' legs, by manful sheafpitchers, by maidens offering trinkets hung on a bough. Teeth chiselling roast meat off the bone—that was medieval enough.

There was a paperback with a big sale called 'Survival Guide'. I don't know what it taught, ignorant as I am, who wondered at first if BAHAI was a medieval form of Barsham and not an Asian teaching of the treasures of silence.

A cloud like a black crab impended; rain fell. Kites with fluttering antennae climbed the returning blue. Influences were propitious for the Zodiac Dance—a thrumming, manic romp; high emblems swaying; horns of Taurus, Sol transcendent, moon-coloured maenads palpitant; cosmic heartbeat; only youth could do it. They trooped away at last. A girl kissed a boy on the emptying green.

Now, farewell Wigmaleeries (dolls' furnishers I think); farewell 'Astrological Service Station', farewell 'Infinity Foods', vendors of 'Tiger Balm: Good for Everything'. Where do they all live, the 'gaudily garlanded'? What are their ordinary days beyond this dream? Bahai, peace be with you: meditate the mystery of a field full of folk transformed again into a field full of cows. For cows life is altogether earnest: they have to keep tearing up grass all day and much of the night to stay alive. As the old farm labourer said: 'What do a cow know of a holiday?'

Farewell Wigmaleeries: welcome back, cows.

※　※　※　※　※　※

THE LONG potato ridges, the blue-black woods, duck flying in pairs: we walked toward the sea. In the last field Suffolk mares stood beautiful and still; 'gentled' as they say in sale catalogues.

We had come through the byways, past my old farm, past the small field where I ploughed the last furrows I ever ploughed with a pair of horses; then along the twisting road to Hulver and Benacre, and to first sight of the sea, with a ship on it. Then a walk among yellow gorse, between lagoons lapping the pebbles at our feet. We sat with Kessingland church tower standing up before us, neither near nor far. Then we had a sandwich, and then a sort of slumber (only it wasn't a slumber) which I mistook for eternity.

Perhaps it was as well that an infantile youth tried to

break his brand-new motor bike by trying to make it climb a sand dune, or I might have been there still. The rumble of the sea in my ears was just an extension of the silence, and a lark sang. I closed my eyes; the breeze which touched my face was like the kiss of life—and I lived.

Walking back through the gay gorse I came on a figure sitting on a tussock transfixed in admiration of a cloud. As I came level with her she turned to me with dazzled eyes and a sidelong smile. 'It reminds me,' she said.

'Reminds you of what, ma'am?' I asked.

'Of my lucky dip.'

'Cold for a bathe, isn't it?'

'I mean the lucky dip at Gorleston where we took our summer holidays when I was a child. On the last day my father used to give me sixpence for the lucky dip.'

'And was yours lucky?'

'The first year I got a doll that leaked sawdust. The second year I got a frog that leaked beans. I even sowed the beans but they didn't grow. Then my father said, "If you didn't choose always the biggest parcel in the tub you might not be disappointed." The next year I put my arm deep in and felt right down to the bottom and chose the smallest thing my fingers met. I undid it and found I had a pretty little bead purse with a fringe, which delighted me. What's more' (she added with a curious look) 'there was a sixpence in it.'

'So your present was free. That was a lucky dip indeed.'

'I've still got it.' She showed it me, with a few beads still attached to the fabric. I saw there was a sixpenny piece inside it. 'You have kept it all this time.'

'Oh no; I spent it at once. I bought a cloud with it,

like that snow-white one I was looking at there. It was our balloon. We sat eating rock in it. I had a friend.'

'So it was a magic purse.' I could not tell her age, but she had lucent green, wide, childlike eyes. 'Is it still a magic purse?'

'Oh yes. There has always been another sixpence when I have spent my last one.' She laid the old purse against her cheek and stroked her face with it. 'I think you understand, sir.'

'The widow's cruse, you mean?'

She nodded. 'It happens for us who have been good lovers, I like to believe.'

'Tryst and trust? That's right.'

She looked at me keenly. 'You, sir, are in love, I think.'

'Yes, I am in love—with life. There's no other way to be, is there?'

'And that's why you picked that bit of bladder-wrack —for a souvenir.'

'You've guessed. And I suppose you feel almost rich now that silver sixpences are rare.'

'Rich,' she nodded. 'Tryst and trust, you said. My man was a silversmith; the poorest silversmith that ever there was. I called him my golden man because of his fair hair: it shone so. They took him away because they said the silver watches he supplied to the hoop-la weren't silver. I have not seen him lately.'

'Your husband?'

'Certainly. We were those childhood friends; we married with a ring he made from one of my sixpences. We found a little church on a common. There was no one, only sparrows. He put it on my finger and said, "It's under God." And I said, "Till death us do part, my golden man." '

'It did part you?'

'I must suppose so.'

'You had a family?'

'All flown like the swallows.'

'You are alone.'

'Sometimes I think I hear the clink of his little hammer. Rich, you said. Yes, rich enough to buy heaven when I hear his tap, tap, tap. But he directs me to the early dewdrop making merry with its rainbow.'

I began to walk on. She rose and walked beside me.

'I'm sure you will find again your golden man,' I told her. 'Tryst and trust, that's it.'

'You should know, sir. And may you have joy of your bit of weed. As my father used to say, "People grope after greatness, but truth lies in the tiniest packet." Fare you well.' She disappeared through a gap in the hedge. I glimpsed a bowery and ancient caravan.

As I hung my bladder-wrack in the porch of my house to foretell rain, I discovered deep in the labyrinth of my heart a germ of envy of the hovel of the green-eyed little woman who had been the girl who groped for the smallest, and now could buy heaven.

❧ ❧ ❧ ❧ ❧ ❧

AFTER TALK, walk: that's essential. After dispersing yourself, go and look for yourself. Where but in this lane? Today clouds hang low over the stubbles, swift and turbid, like 'Iser rolling rapidly'. The same old lane, but always different; the sky above it, the ground under it. Today it has enormous puddles; here and there its verges run with farmyard liquors brown as ale. A little while ago dust was drifted to either side softer than a carpet; just the thing to walk on for a tramp. Or pilgrim.

I am always going on a long, long pilgrimage when I close my garden gate behind me. But in a few miles I am turning to find the wind in my face, after a seeming lifetime of speculation on those clouds like Iser rolling rapidly; and on the weeds at my feet. Yellow toadflax is peeking out of the wreckage of willow-herb: starveling buttercups lean from the roadside grass, still contriving to be gay.

It poured with rain all day. At five it let up, and I took the road. Then another million gallons was found secreted in that sky, which poured it down with the effect of a coarse-rose watering-can. Hard drops went snip-snap against my mac, and tinkled in the puddles. An intense silence was over the fields; not a machine hummed anywhere.

I passed a farm. Even the dogs did not bark. Here they usually greet me. One is wire-haired: when he barks he levitates himself: every bark jumps all four paws an inch in air, body stiff: he even jumps himself askew. The other is a black retriever, with a sinewy tail: it really seems to wag the dog. They are friendly: they sort of laugh while they bark: 'It's just part of our job to do this, you understand: wuff-wuff!' While Ginger vibrates in front of me, his mate sniffs my shoes and follows behind, padding silently.

But today not a stir, not a sound. Fair-weather dogs? Rain makes vivid all smells; green smells of nettles, of

66

wild mint; black ones of farmyard manure rich and ripe; now a wraith of wood smoke entwines with it. Wood smoke and farmyard manure make a bitter-sweet blend, acceptable to me; robust enough to disinfect an air polluted by the speeches of politicians with little to communicate but sneers at one another. We are no longer merely indifferent: we get positively to hate the lot of them, do Tom, Dick and I. The only positive good sense, the only recipe for revival, is talked by the farmers— that in any case we need to double the output of England's still fertile soil.

Growth of populations stresses a need for bigger, better farms? Dear friends, arms and legs on small plots of this earth can produce vastly more than your soil-compressing giant tractors. Look at allotments: at country gardens. And the record yield of wheat this year was grown on a three-acre plot. Yes, this I say, when I look at my own small vegetable plot; and read of a friend and his wife returning laden with good things from their allotment on September 21.

'Broccoli umbrageous'—inspired phrase of his, I thought, as I struggled to stake, prop, tie our own sprouting broccoli, which seem afflicted with gigantism. After the gales I surveyed what looked like a panic of green flounces that had waltzed themselves inebriate, and had toppled the Brussels sprouts, too. Every leaf seemed to hold a pint of rain. This is the result on ground which was first under a deep-litter hut for hens, then a store for fertiliser: a nitrogenous intoxication. Is there any way to sedate a kitchen garden?

My sister and her husband came to lunch and enjoyed our courgettes with chicken pie and my wife's brown beer. They brought us a basin of eggs from their freest of free-range hens. These have a broad paddock to roam. They were bought as culls from battery cages; they had even to re-learn to walk. Now they are sprightly, happy all day long, and lay copiously.

My sister brought me also those first editions of H. G. Wells which I last read aged eighteen in my father's study: 'The Passionate Friends', 'Marriage', 'Tono Bungay', all those sociological love themes of poor research scientist and spoilt little rich girl. What a diet of 'free love' 1912-style, to feed an impressionable youth. And I wrote 'Wellsian' letters from the farm to that sweet large-eyed girl I left behind me in our suburb. What did she make of them, I wonder? I can almost get back into his skin, re-reading 'Marriage', in which the couple went all the way to Labrador 'to think'. Why go to Labrador to 'think'? How Wellsian.

Why not think on High Common? Where better than in the quiet of this lane in the rain? Look at that tree stippled with old-fashioned creamy apples, and geese sitting dreaming with their beaks turned backwards; and that mottled cock arguing with two hens in front of him, 'Tut, tut; what's the point of staying out here in the rain, girls: let's go in.'

The farmer has felled several yards of hedge at the dog-legged corner; and the young heifers that inhabit that pasture come to the wire he has put up and gaze down the lane: it has become a 'room with a view' for Friesian maidens. Their deep-bodied mothers graze elsewhere. I stop to admire them as I pass; they look so comfortable: 'in full profit' as is the phrase at auctions.

'Marriage' à la Wells and Motherhood à la moo: I

68

recall yesterday driving between cars double-parked where children were coming out of school. Mothers arriving in a hurry looked rather teeth-gritted and grim I thought. They are just at the age of maximum infant-fatigue, yet young enough to recall the glamorous courting days, the dancing cheek to cheek. I have just read a segment of a new Durrell romance in 'The Times'. How his heroines rush to feel under a young man's shirt for his heart, and lay cold fingers on his flesh. Never in my youth, never were fingers laid over my warm heart. We were too well brought up. After one marvellous evening I did dare to beg a kiss—'even just a peck', I urged.

'Well,' she said. 'Just a peck.' And it was. And after all those Wellsian letters. Ah, Mabel.

MABEL: A name murdered by being rhymed with 'table' —but never laughable to me since, as teenagers, we sheltered from an April shower. Drops sparkling through young leaves striped her cheeks like tears. Her eyes, large, wondering, unawakened to the world, shone under the lamps of Bycullah Avenue, fitfully on account of branches swaying under the globes. I recall the feel of her waist as we sat out a dance on the stairs. That's all; just the firm grace of the flesh under an evening frock, without any foundation garment, as yet.

She married and had a family; then at fifty (I was told) she slipped on her rockery, and fell—and died. My hand still has the impression of her girl's waist; now simply the pleasure a potter might have in feeling his vessel taking shape; the supple form; a moment of life.

But that's long past—except for my right hand's remembrance. Hands can have better memories than minds, I believe. And now here I am taking down bean poles, dismantling that green arras of leaves and coral flowers, which bounded the far end of our plot. How often have I sat looking the length of our crops and enjoyed the sight of it, while gnats danced in the level rays of a summer evening? I pack the poles away: it is slightly sad, taking down bean bines, like saying goodbye to a summer friend; and for no reason at all remembering Mabel to whom I wrote those H. G. Wellsian letters, after reading 'The Passionate Friends', aged 18 both of us. The stiffer one grows, the more nimbly thoughts glide in and out among the years.

❋ ❋ ❋ ❋ ❋ ❋

OUR HOME is two miles of crinkum-crankum from my rural post-box. Much closer as the crow flies, if only I were a crow, or a Boy Scout of my generation who wore a gallant hat and carried a stout stave with which he could leap ditches. But I'm not. I plod the lane which wanders like a river.

But who would miss a yard of it? Deep-bodied cows graze and go on grazing; but the donkey who grazes with them comes trotting to the fence and wags his ears at me: 'Haw—how-de-do?' I pause, put the tips of my fingers together, in an Asian sort of greeting, nod my head. We understand one another.

On my right they are harvesting sugar beet in the old

way, since the soil is too saturated for the machines to work. A family farm can muster a team and cope, whatever the weather. On the left, land draining is going on in the new way : bulldozers lift shingle in their jaws and release it with a noise like avalanches. In the gateway mud is enormous : every time the broad tyres churn it, great new mud cheeses are rolled out, stamped with the trade mark of rubber. To my right—between avalanches —the crisp chop of beet knives can be heard. Tidy heaps of the tops lie in rows, a clean and green ration for the herd. They grow sweeter as they wilt.

I pass circles of silvery ash where lately Guy Fawkes was burned yet again—one mounted on an old sofa. Oddly, these two miles seem a longer distance in a car than on foot. I think, because it is not so much the time taken as how you like to take your time. I come in view of a great spread of land to my right, that lambent view of ploughed and sown : inch-high rows of winter wheat emerging like a resurrection of the stubbles. The eyes lose count of minutes at footpace through all this : the heart expands to the old earth story.

    ❧   ❧   ❧   ❧   ❧   ❧

WE PUT our two glasses of country wines together. 'Look at these tones of nature.' Lamps of the sun; red and golden.

We went into the Craft Shop beside the Butter Cross. It looked cornucopian. In the middle was a great loose bunch of wild grasses, oats, barley; a sort of harvest festival flourish. On the wall were corn dollies in the shape of horseshoes, traditional to Suffolk. But having my eyes blurred by a shower, I saw them as croissants fresh from the oven. And mugs and cups and saucers of a light brown ware ... Well, they call it biscuit, don't they?

I saw rings made from silver threepenny-bits, engraved with '3D' and a king's head; obverse and reverse: choose which you like. They were made by a silversmith living in a Norfolk village. I chose '3D'; it brought me memories of Christmas puddings and my grandfather muttering of the German menace. This one is dated 1917, when the German menace was on us.

There were corn dollies and dolls; big dolls and little Thumbelina dolls. Ranged on a shelf above were patch-work cushions whose vegetable dyes echoed those tints that were in our sunshot country wines. I gazed around; all here was the work of human hands busy in cottages within a circuit whose centre was this small town. If so much could be gathered just here, what a vast amount of hand work must be going on all over the land. Hands are alive and variable. The perfect machine product is perfectly boring. The things displayed here all had their spark of life, just as my former wooden plough had life, because, being hand-made, it varied slightly from every other plough. Husbandry also is a craft. May I too be called a craftsman, to whom that miniature harvest festival in the middle of the shop symbolised the fields of my farm labour: the restless oats opening their awns to show the ivory oats dangling, a field of wheat brown as a crust of bread: these sights had been also a reward of hard labour; and in winter frost furring a single straw by my boot as I milked. I write with a local goose-quill.

whereby I vote myself into the company of craftsmen.

I bought a water-colour paintbox, and a small stuffed duck, bright yellow with an orange beak. My paintbox represents an ambition. Mrs. H. aspires to the Academy; she can make a collapsed barn look apocalyptic. I aspire to be hung upstairs in the Craft Shop. A companionable sketcher said: 'If you take lessons you'll be taught tricks.' I taught myself to write: how else to learn no tricks?

Pictures are upstairs in a room looking out over the Butter Cross at a graceful 17th-century female on its dome holding evenly balanced scales. Rather Hans Andersenish to me, this steep little house which is the Craft Shop; perhaps a home for Gerda and Kay of 'The Snow Queen'. Listen for footsteps at night: the place is a pedestrian precinct. Hans Andersen could have evolved fairy tales around these things: a 'Threepenny Wedding' for Thumbelina perhaps. Who would have put the silver 3p ring on her finger? Why: the Boy (Stevenson's) who sitting up in bed 'sees before him dale and plain; the pleasant Land of Counterpane'. Limpid dyes illumine these patchwork squares ranged on a shelf above the dolls: they are his fields of grass and grain.

The Old Maid in the tale of 'The Bottle Neck' saw from her attic window a balloon sailing over the little town. In my mind I see Thumbelina fleeing with the Counterpane Boy through the dusk from Farmer Bull, who has been promised her in marriage by her stepmother. He is a gross red man who boasts he gets what he wants just when he wants it. And he wants her now, immediately. In a perverse mood once Thumbelina said, 'I admire that sort of man,' which hurt the Boy that loved her, who was poor. She regretted those words and now hated

73

Farmer Bull; but her stepmother insisted that she kept to her hasty acceptance. The young lovers hoping to elude Farmer Bull fled to an abandoned chapel in a thicket, in which they had trysted. The Boy slipped the 'threepenny ring' on her finger just as Farmer Bull entered the porch in pursuit of them.

A soldier with a bandaged head suddenly appeared, barring the way. He took Thumbelina and the Boy by their hands, led them out past the dumbfounded farmer, past graves and yews and cypresses, until they came to a dim form swelling out above the headstones. It was a balloon. He lifted them into the basket. Farmer Bull now came running and grabbed Thumbelina. She cried out. The soldier drew a pistol. Bull fled in terror: they heard him fall into a flooded ditch with a loud splash.

Said the soldier, 'The threepenny piece on your ring was in my pocket when I was shot down. But the balloon will bear you safely, never fear. Your imagination will never let you fall while you live for each other.' The soldier with the bandaged head then melted away: the balloon rose. The Old Maid of 'The Bottle Neck' whose betrothed had been slain long ago waved to the lovers from her attic as they floated over her town in the dawn; then away across the Land of Counterpane, watching its fields of green and brown and its lakes of blue glide past beneath them, even as we do who have a lover's dreams to keep us ...

Wake up: the Craft Shop is closing for the night. Come, my little yellow duck. You suddenly mean much to me. In a pub I saw couples wistful in brief meetings. On my way home I passed two lovers hugged into a hollow tree. Above them a white fine-weather cloud was

74

a balloon, gay and out of reach. Sit here on my shelf, little Easter duckling, staring across to my writing table. A storm bursts on the window-pane: the outside world is spiteful with hail, like the mood of which Thumbelina repented only just in time. I need inspiration, little duckling, as the Boy needed consolation for the thought of Thumbelina ever favouring Farmer Bull. Nothing airy-fairy, just your bulgy comic eyes and orange beak to sustain me.

❦ ❦ ❦ ❦ ❦ ❦

A FRIEND came to lunch with a blackberrying expedition in view. And he brought a bottle of champagne. After which he and my wife set off with baskets, and I went to sleep. Who is it speaks of 'golden slumbers'? I had them. I had explained I was by nature a blackberry non-picker. But rather a loitering, cloud-gazing companion to the blackberry-picker, picking one blackberry and eating two—one from her basket.

But I too had a fruit in view, a picking. By nature I am an ardent nutter. October is my birth month: Libra is my sign. In October I walk; and in my mind I nut. But how few nuts hang on the hazels in these hedges. In fact, as good as none, to my eyes. So many of next year's tiny catkins; so few of this year's nuts.

I said to myself, perhaps in a hedge they are over-crowded. I will grow my own nut tree. I trimmed the hazel stub beside my pond and tutored just one stem upward. I pruned away its side shoots, and left it with a head of young branches. By midsummer I began to see nuts. As summer advanced I counted them daily. I counted fifteen in all. Next morning they were gone. My wife had said she feared the birds would have them. I looked hard: gradually these nuts reappeared; first one tight bunch, then another; until I accounted for all fifteen. Green hazel nuts are perfect in camouflage. Again and again I said to myself: 'The birds really have had them now.' Again, bunch by bunch they reappeared. My looking had to be something like a meditation.

As October came in they turned to a toasted colour at the tips. They were easier to spot as they hung over the pond.

'While you will be blackberrying I will be nutting,' I said.

'Don't fall in the water,' were her last instructions to me.

For my token nutting I took a small basket which our neat-fingered neighbour had woven to contain my pen-wiper. It is about the size of a song-thrush's nest. If you write with a quill you do emphatically need a pen-wiper. A pen-wiper stood on the manager's table in Barclays Bank, Bury St. Edmunds, in 1924; as I have no doubt one then stood on the table of every bank manager in the realm. We had entered to seek an overdraft (who didn't?). This was granted us, with monitions against frittering our days shooting and hunting.

We should have been in a chastened mood; but as his door closed on us our first words were, 'What bits of him do you think his pen-wiper was composed of?' A pen-wiper was a sartorial rag fair of its owner. Snippets of suitings were sewn to a central button.

So I took this basket the size of a thrush's nest to pick

my nuts into. I advanced to the edge of the pond and reached for the nuts now visibly offering themselves, smooth and grained like timber, fixed back-to-back in threes and fours. I had never counted more than fifteen; but I plucked two dozen, which just about filled my basket. I had reserved for my birthday this small rite, this token nutting.

My wife's warning was on account of the fact that the evening before, I had upset a newly watered pot plant while she was pouring a drink to celebrate the morrow. While I watered the plant I was demanding not a birth-day, but 'a birth-week', because it took me most of that time to get born, according to my mother.

Thus I spoke, when—crash—over went the pot plant. She downed sherry bottle and ran to get things to wipe up the mess of earth and plant and water. This done she resumed her pouring. I took my filled glass, sat myself heartily back in the old easy chair with a cry of, 'Here's to us, after 40 years!' and the tip of my left elbow sent a standard lamp reeling to the floor with din and instant darkness.

'One—Two—and now for Three,' she cried. 'These things go in threes.'

I fetched a new bulb, restored the light, fixed its dented shade back on its head. Again, 'Here's to us.' And here, after all, was to us, but a bit muted now.

Would it not be more than possible I should fall into the pond the next day, to make accident number Three of three in a row? But I did not: I have the crop of my little nut tree safely before me in Sighile's basket that is the size of a thrush's nest. I don't know where the household nutcrackers are: they were part of a wedding gift from my aunt from Buenos Aires, and are in the form of a pair of female legs of brass. They are not apparent at the moment. But I don't at the moment wish to crack the nuts—just to look at them as some old Dutch painter of still life must have stared at nuts peeping from their sheaths' raggle-taggle edges. Much joy he had in their hue and texture, his picture shows. Truly to live, I think one must be in love with somebody or something—say a basketful of fresh-picked hazel nuts.

❧   ❧   ❧   ❧   ❧   ❧

ALL THAT rain swimming down the downhill lane, and all that fire-coloured foliage: another summer is at the end of its tether, quite literally. 'Flood', says notice; 'wash', say the countryfolk. The chains of puddles became almost two continuous canals: a narrow camber of tarmac between them itself was wrinkled with water's satin-like skin. The flanking hedges looked gay under the grey sky.

The maples are pure flame. I picked one leaf; and I thought of a child's cheek who has been roasting chestnuts at the fire. Yellow shield-shaped leaves are strung across some blackened brambles. Nature is acting a carnival; bunting soaked but obstinately gay: the rain pours down: testudos of umbrellas raise a cheer for the shivering queen and her maids of honour smiling bravely. I see it all in these October hedges, the tarmac black as those umbrellas, rain swimming off them, the criss-cross silver of its flow.

The wind is cold and bustling: to my mind it is a

Neverland allegory of that typically English occasion which earns the caption: 'Rain did not dampen Yartoft Carnival spirit.' Nor mine; it's a singing day: dun sky, black road, flaring hedges.

The wind has at me round the blind, empty cottages by the bridge. Yet a six-feet tall sere grass stem still stands up, having withstood a gale which felled a tree. Our friend Sighile, on seeing any sad blank house, red-brick, unpicturesque, confesses to a yearning to make it homely and happy, as if it were a lost dog or cat. We too have said at times: 'That could be a home,' and the more raw, blank and blind it looked the more imagination has gone to work on it. Did not our two Italian prisoners in the war greet with delight our nag's stable and harness-room, crying: 'In Italy this be good house.' And they made it their home while they worked on our farm. And wept when they left.

Even a wooden shed which Bert and I built in 1942 to house a cow, appeals to me in some way as I pass it today, still apparently as sound as ever. How well Bert built it of hedge saplings and boards. It is not mine any more, yet it is still mine in thought. I am for ever sitting on a three-legged stool in there, milking a cow called Star, or feeding my hens or my two pigs. That hut is to me what Thoreau's hut was to him by Walden pond. One could live in it, I dream, and expand the hours by loitering and looking—and maybe hoeing beans. I used to sit in it quite a lot, looking out of the hatch door as I milked, and not hurrying, because I enjoyed the view of the grass and trees it framed.

The wind is now lashing those nailed-up red brick cottages by the bridge here. They stand slightly above the meeting of three ways, gazing, if their windows were not blind, along the low road where gravity almost ceases to impel the flow of three watercourses, met there in one swirl that wrestles with itself, and spills across the pasture and the lane at 'the wash'. Yes, gazing straight along it would be those windows blinkered with tin.

There is hardly any hovel so mean but someone might say: 'That could be my retreat, my refuge.' There was just one, I recall, of which my wife said: 'That at any rate is past redemption.' But it wasn't. It now has casement windows, new thatch, a rose-bower porch. Wood smoke rises from its chimney, whose savour sweetens briefly the interior of our car as we pass. Even the stockade of faggots within which I chopped kindling felt homely, gipsyish, warm.

So these brick cottages I pass at the meeting of the ways and the waters, whipped now by wind and rain, have an appeal in spite of tin blinkers. There is a life to be lived here, watching the waters bubbling out from under the bridge and away in triple spate. A pied wagtail is on the roof: he looks at home there, jerking and peeking, shrugging off the rain.

Anyhow, they are doing something to the farmhouse on the hill, I see. The first time I saw it was at this time of year, but on a calm day. It was empty. Rooks were calling in the high trees beside it. A mound in a thicket struck me as mysterious; and since then I have been told it is prehistoric. But more mysterious to me was the fact that the place was in the possession of turkeys. They paraded slowly on the front lawn and the drive, with a decorous yet rather menacing quietude, as of Compton-Burnett Victorians in bombazine and broadcloth. They met, nodded their big beaks, passed on. It might have been a funeral party bewitched into great sad birds. I felt an urge to go up to one and say: 'Madam, can you tell me who...?'

Sometimes a moment occurs when we say: 'I have been here before: I have been one of this party, and somebody is going to say ... I know just what they are going to say ... No, I forget.' I was wafted through the Looking-Glass for a split second, among its all-too human animals.

The farmhouse begins to look cheerful, businesslike. There will be children playing instead of prowling turkeys. But I still get an eerie feeling when I remember that silent garden party of turkeys.

※　　※　　※　　※　　※　　※

7 A.M. AS if back from the Wood of Second Chances—and the garden strewn with leaves—awake! Silent house; tray of tea by my bed. Awake: be yourself! Through the window I see the seat under my beech tree being pelted by hail.

Set in its beechen corner, between beech and holly, I mind it well in June, and sitting on it, my feet in daisies. Before me the first roses, on my left, through a window formed by two boughs, is my pond, a sluggish water, but glimmering like a freshet at the touch of swallows. It is muddy, like an enlarged ditch, but in June puts on pride by a resurrection of water lilies.

There we received visitors; not formally expected; but a stranger who put her head over the gate saying, 'I was born here in 1917.' And a man who appeared and said, 'I

81

was born here 70 years ago today.' He had two brothers with him. They ran about the garden like boys. No, did not run, being elderly, and one a bit lame—but their eagernesses ran: they were boys again crying, 'Here's where the cherry tree stood; and we climbed it to pick the cherries first thing of a morning. And here was the other walnut tree' (being a mossed stump). 'And hereabout was the big pear tree; and we used to pick the pears and lob them up to you, brother, through the window, when you had been naughty and sent to bed supperless. Look, the old apple tree's still standing ... There was a holly ...'

What with the trees that stand before us now and those trees which they made us see standing here in their memory, we began to feel we were not so much in a garden as in a wood of trees past and present—like that Wood of Second Chances which suddenly conjured itself before the astonished gaze of Mr. Lob's guests on midsummer eve in that play of Barrie's called 'Dear Brutus'. Into this wood with its moonlight and shadows wandered these dissatisfied people in evening dress, and there they found themselves in quite different clothes and lives and relationships—even the butler. Yet they themselves did not change in their behaviour. Except one, who was no longer an old soak, but young and jolly, with a beloved 12-year-old daughter beside him in this wood. But then the moonlight darkened, and out of the darkness came the daughter's voice, 'Don't leave me, Daddy! I don't want to be—a might-have-been.'

I saw this play in its first week. Wonderful stagecraft it was. I was young, just 24; and the daughter Margaret was to me just shadowy. But now, waking from a memory of it, and seeing under my eyes in this morning's paper the words Family Planning, I say to myself, 'To think of the people to whom I may have denied a life—glad life, sad life, suffering life—but Life.

'Now why are you staring at your summer seat, and the weather playing dice on it with small white cubes of hail, and are suddenly seized with this thought just because you have been reading Barrie's play; and see, as a result of summer's lookers-over-the-hedge, a ghostly wood of all the trees they climbed for cherries, nuts and pears three score years ago?'

Family Planning: what a phrase. A man and a woman are not just themselves: they are gateways to posterity. That seemed a trite thought until I recalled that cry from the darkening stage, 'I don't want to be a might-have-been!' How grudging a gateway to Life has my life been?

Look how the dead leaves are drifted round our summer seat. I know all the ways of the leaves, their scurryings to and fro in the winds. Their drifts are the tides of air made visible. They dance round the old pear stump in the same circuit every November, while above them on the stump the great red rose whose name I do not know still blooms. She bears loose floppy roses: they reel in the gusts: she is a *dolce vita* rose. But under her velvet petals, what thorns!

On a rare noon of calm sun it is still possible to sit on the seat and see the leaves in the patterns of their pauses. But soon the wind starts them on their whispering dance again, walnut, beech, sycamore. I shiver and go indoors. In the latest gust the last red rose is scattering herself among the dancers; her sumptuous petals scampering among the horse-coloured dead leaves.

But I can still sit in my sun-house when a low ray reaches in, and watch my last vine leaves, as splendid as any, and two small bunches of grapes I left on the vine for tokens. Next year I shall have a roof of this rampant vine; and I shall call it my vine house, and forget the children I never had, and the second chances I could not have taken, knowing I should always react in the same way. Which is what I mean when I say, 'Be yourself,' that it is merely a phrase to jerk me out of bed. Whether I were a don or a gipsy, I would still sing with old Wyatt:

> 'Nothing on earth more would I have,
> Save, that I have, to have it still.'

'FOR ALL flesh is as grass, and all the glory of man as the flower of grass. The grass withereth, and the flower thereof falleth away.' But lovely is the grass that withereth and falleth not away. Walking, staring at the clouds, at the ploughland, at next year's harvest which is already greening the harrowed earth, I suddenly saw it on the tousled common, between the lane and a black thicket—just grass, tall, sere, upstanding, with bowed filigree of empty flower heads; very thin, dry stalks, ghost-like, yet strong enough to stand up sapless through all these gales and rain. Pale grey they rise out of the rich browns of a tangle of soaked willow-herb, such a depth of brown tints as a painter would use all of his palette to express, or try to express.

'Unpaintable!' cried Alfred Munnings of a certain oak tree in the landscape, in a fit of grand inspirational despair. And a fallen chestnut leaf could give that supremely successful artist the same feeling of helplessness.

But I have arrived at my halfway house. Let me see if the gate is closed. There is a little chain that drops through a staple in the post, a chain with a shank like my great-uncle's watch chain which he threaded through a special buttonhole in his waistcoat. Would this chain rebuff a straying beast? It would not debar an angel nor an elf. But I knew a farmer who stretched a single bramble shoot across a gap in his hedge and attached the loose end with a piece of binder twine. And presumably prayed or spoke a spell, for no cow broke past that green strand during the rush of harvest. Perhaps this little chain has its spell: after all, what would our ancestors have said of an electric fence?

If the chain is through the staple, it means Sighile is at home, and there will be a cup of tea to refresh me for the second half of my walk. If not, I have permission to rest in a basket chair under her veranda.

Past the gate is a path of small bright gravel that looks like kibbled nuts. In August I surprised a horde of sparrows there: a brown broth of wings whirled up around my head: they had alighted to peck gravel to grind the corn in their crops which they had gleaned from the stubbles. Today the last chestnut leaf of summer hung on her young tree, crisp as a curled wafer, containing in itself the whole palette of autumn as in a narrow dish.

'Look,' I said of this leaf. I have a habit of picking up some simple object that is full of light, and proffering it to a kindred spirit—a wet pebble, or one of those tiny striped empty snailshells through which the light shows as through a horn lantern, such as I keep on my mantel-shelf for months, until a flick of the duster ... Even one of those new-minted tiny coins that I think of as farthings glittering like gold: this, too, is accepted as being precious.

Likewise I enjoy that little chain on the gate: it is so different from most of the gate fitments I meet; the bolts and hooks, the spring catches that once caught but catch no more, the bolts that miss their shafts by an inch that's as good as a yard, the hook now too high or too low for its eye, gate and gatepost having lost their liaison owing to subsidence or collision with a wheel. But this little chain is always apt and easy; and the clap-to foot of the gate rests on a small wooden block, which looks like the very reticence of forethought.

She accepted the last chestnut leaf as understandingly as if it were an illuminated scroll, which in a sense it was; and I received a cup of tea. Admittedly it was her leaf, but it acted like a gift in that when two pairs of eyes focus on one thing they tend to remember it. There was a shared chestnut leaf in Munnings's life, which is mem-orable for the fact that he put it in his book 'An Artist's Life'.

Thus: 'A Hungarian sculptor without a penny had been walking with me in the park ... we spoke little; we had only French in common. He had picked up a large perfect yellow leaf. Looking at me with melancholy brown eyes, he said: "Munnings, elle est très belle." "Ah, oui, très belle," said I, and we sighed ...'

Faced with that leaf, the successful painter and the failed sculptor felt equally humble. Those who knew

86

of Munnings only as a boisterous extrovert may not have guessed at his essential modesty in the presence of nature.

'What is it all for?' he asked me, 'all our struggle to paint, to write?' as we sat in an ancient little country church we had found. Only a sparrow in the roof answered.

Munnings was a countryman by birth. But did he ever put a spade into the earth, for all his milling and farming upbringing? I doubt it. But in our lane behind our gates, peculiarly fastened both of ours, we are occupied with the earth: we dig, we sow, we gather into store sheds and freezers. Nature is a challenge to the artist, but she is a partner to us gardeners. We pause at the illumination of the last chestnut leaf, watched by four eyes of four hens (they eye us sideways), but we do not sigh over it. We go on to talk of eggs, of artichokes, and rosebuds that are still summery. The nearest I ever come to the grand despair of a Munnings is when one of my biggest potatoes so carefully stored is found to be rotten.

❧ ❧ ❧ ❧ ❧ ❧

A THING like a green sedan chair is perched high on something yellow that glimmers through the bare hedge like a gigantic tiger. It has got itself into a corner opposite my gate. At intervals during the last two days a sort of stripped-down pram is wheeled along the lane and poked into the hedge beside this object. Thence issue sharp blue flames, then a burst of orange fireworks.

Then silence: then a steady hammering.

It is a fact that the most sophisticated machines now on the land, equipped with every hydraulic device, at some time require to be hit hard with a hammer. Nothing escapes the hammer; the cleverest machine will one day echo to it, art and hogs come under it. This huge device which is controlled from that aerial sedan chair, is simply to drain that field, along with attendant tractors and trailers. That field is just about the acreage of Redisham Glebe, which bordered my paddock when I lived there. And Charlie drained all that field with a set of hand tools in 1941, by himself. Having lived with it he knew exactly where the 'fall' was, although the field looked quite flat. It was surrounded by a thorn hedge. When Charlie had laid all the pipes to his satisfaction, he cut the thorn hedge and laid the long straight thorns in the trench above them, pressing them down with a special small fork, and then shovelled the earth back level. When I watch these great machines I think of Charlie on Redisham Glebe; just his two arms and legs—and the know-how.

I was back there the other day. Only the land has not changed, and the small wooden byre Bert built with stout pieces from that glebe hedge for uprights. I think of Bert, and then of Reggie passing on his bike with his terrier in the basket on the handlebars: man and dog were inseparable. Then of Annie driving her three cows along the road to pasture with a wand of green willow for fly-whisk. She sang a little song: they moved slowly, grazing the grass of the verge as they went to their pasture.

Next—the figure of my wife, as I approached the

back door, her hands outspread: 'The well has gone dry again.' That would be at the beginning of haysel, almost to the day.

'If you want to know what Redisham really is—or was, go and look at that field opposite the church,' I told the lady with the TV team. It had been freshly ploughed. Its furrows glinted. It was motionless yet it looked to be all of a move, like a darkly glittering sea.

'The best field in Redisham.' I am back 30 years, sitting in the church porch awaiting the Reverend; looking at its new furrows glistening in the winter sun; sitting there with Ness, who walked so erect. 'Yes, that's the best field in Redisham,' we agreed.

There were no 'amenities', but there was the earth. There was no telly, but we talked of the soil—the "arth'. We talked of 'mowlds'. Bert made the mowlds of clay, with long patience of digging and ridging, so his acre became like fine fen land, and he grew master crops of spuds, and kale and onions and beans. Today those mowlds cry out for sun, for air: Bert is dead; they suffocate under concrete: a petrol pump stands in place of his store-shed: the petrol pump is king.

I stood in the graveyard near where Ness now lies, and within a yard of Bert where he lies; Bert, who with me built my byre: Bell's byre, Bell's hennery, Bell's hog-house: Three in one. All around, the grass was still verdant: it waved in the breeze. Bert used to scythe it with his famous scythe, the blade keen and thin and kinky: there was a tale to every nick, of some hidden thing harder than grass which had taken a bite of it. I rather revered his work with it, the epic of a man's body.

Bert swung his scythe over and around the grave

89

mounds, revealing ancient names of headstones: 'Eliza-beth, beloved wife of ... died ... 1805': soon haycocks stood among his forefathers.

'Aren't you going into the church?' I asked the camera team today.

'The light isn't good enough' ('And the life was the light of men').

Oh, how impossible to 'do' Redisham in minutes. 'Put your sound machine against the medieval latch, while I turn that old ringle—the sound it makes ... kling-klang, echoing into the nave: that's Redisham: kling-klang every Sunday for years and years ... Well, do at any rate take a picture of that ploughed field opposite, and a close-up of those savage crested furrows ...' They did that.

'I shall ask you two questions' (said the producer) ... 'Please keep looking at me: don't move your head ...' The camera was focused. I put my two feet on the spots indicated: just there and there: left foot, right foot. OK. Now ...

How impossible to reawaken a sense of what the vil-lage of my Apple Acre was as I knew it: how to signify to that fish-eye of the camera lens that for one thing, I was standing a pace from my old friend Bert peacefully sleeping in earth ... and recalling the familiar cry, 'The well's gone dry again' ... and the handle of the tall iron pump over the sink hanging loose as an arm broken at the shoulder.

❦ ❦ ❦ ❦ ❦ ❦

I REALISE we were the last people who lived in that old home in the old way. That is to say, with kitchen and scullery as originally planned. The 'scullery' came in with 'gentility' in the mid-eighteenth century. By 1914 every little suburban semi had a scullery: it meant that a maid was kept, and the kitchen did as her sitting room. The big farm house had no scullery, but a great kitchen and a dairy.

Even Redisham's Victorian vicarage (in a living worth altogether £150 a year) boasted a scullery; and a green baize door to shut the servants' quarters from the genteel front hall. Maids were once kept, but not by us. We took off the green baize door (I still have it). Otherwise, we lived in the house as we found it in 1938. For why? In the scullery stood the copper, which would be bubbling in the corner where now stands a freezer. That did the washing for a family of five, and in the war six or seven. Sticks and logs were burned in the 'copper hole': it was gross extravagance to burn coal. 'The sort of woman who burns coal in her copper hole.' Say no more.

The sink was in the scullery, and that tall pump which ceased work every June when the well went dry; also the soft-water pump, with an iron knob as big as a cricket ball on the end of its handle. Boots were ranged in the scullery. A Londoner who stayed with us during the war said: 'I shall always think of this house as the "House of Boots".' Redisham soil was clinging. The scullery floor was of brick: the kitchen floor was of brick. They were scrubbed once a week; and until they dried we had to tiptoe across in our socks. A kettle sang on the hob in the kitchen; a home-cured ham hung in the pantry, off a pig fed in my hog-house in the paddock.

The scullery was multi-purpose: it was essential for that semi-heroic exertion of the weekly wash; the copper was also the house's hot-water system, until a leggy bath was put in a bedroom and a tank installed in the roof. It took 400 strokes of the iron pump to fill that tank, when there was water in the well. That was my job daily. As I did it I reflected that progress was not necessarily labour-saving.

The old vicarage is a lovely house today, with traditional wood fires in iron baskets, where we had only two black iron stoves jutting into the rooms for maximum heat and economy. The hall and stairs look much more spacious now, with wall-to-wall carpeting. We could only afford a meagre strip: it was a long, long trail a-winding from bedrooms to kitchen, a narrow grey trail between black-varnished deal, which, of course, narrowed the passage and stairs to the eye.

Nevertheless, happiness was enjoyed there: it was a house of children. It is again a house of children; and it had been a house of children in the 1870s, a vicar's daughter of 85 wrote and told me. I think every country vicarage was meant to be a house of children.

'I can only remember being happy there,' says our daughter, now 35.

The scullery today has become a beautiful labour-saving kitchen. But it could not banish its former self from my mind's eye. I shall always see it as the scullery:

the copper, the wringer, the cast-iron pumps, the boots.

In those days the road past the vicarage was roamed by Mr. Pearse's pigs foraging under the oaks for acorns : Clarence's cows grazed the roadside grass as they dawdled to their pasture, touched by Annie's leafy wand. Think simply of the economy of that half-mile, on a national scale : feed that was home-grown : our forefathers knew all about that. The oak trees have long been felled : it is a fairly fast road now, dangerous to cows and instant death to pigs.

Farewell, old family home. Back now to the crink-crank lane which has been my home for 10 years, and this old oddly-cum-homely farmhouse. Cows can still graze a wayside common here. There is High Common, there is Blacksmith's Common, there is Great Common, there is Mill Common, beyond which Sighile's roof crouches among its apple trees, and its garden's trim internal hedges which have abrupt turns of an Alice-in-Wonderland inconsequence; as if they led to that all-important Nowhere which is where the very young, and the people like me who fool other people into thinking we are old, most want to be. There are clues to it : there are forms and faces if you have eyes for them, shapes gnomelike and gnarled. Every leaf has its dance. I left Annie's farmhouse in Redisham where a kettle was singing on the hob : I come to Sighile's and find a kettle singing on the hob. Open an iron door of her range and a fire licks a red tongue at you. Beside the hob we hobnob over cups of tea. Two gardens and an agricultural lane are a subject to outwear time. We had been talking of digging potatoes.

'And then,' I said, 'I went down on my knees ...'

She laughed aloud: 'To pray?'

'No, with a trowel, to dig for them the way archaeologists dig for shards, scraping around gingerly ...'

I have tried every method of digging potatoes without damage; spade, big fork, small fork, 2-tined fork, even trowel. They are wound-prone. The damage done in machine-lifting must be immense, if my doing it by hand led to such a casualty list. Indeed, I might have prayed: 'O god of spuds, let not this thrust slice a beauty.'

So out again into the eye of the sun blinking low through bare boughs. On to the post box on Took's Common. Who was Took? And who awarded his memory a common? How does one achieve to have one's name commemorated in a common? I would rather that than be made a life peer, which is not saying much, since to be ermined would be to me a fate worse than death. And the public loses track of birth names: who was this Lord Honkytonk? We never can remember.

I have missed the post, loitering by the ruined forge in memory of my Kitty, Prince and Boxer, so often shod there. What matter? Tomorrow is a day.

❧ ❧ ❧ ❧ ❧ ❧

THE GREAT machines have rumbled away from the fields they have been draining, with a final stirring of prodigious mud: farm horses could create nothing to equal it, not even in the mating season. Mud, glorious mud. Ten thousand gallons of soup in a tureen the size of a field gateway. Thick or clear? Consommé or potage?

94

Oh, bless the French: potage of course. Soup of the evening, beautiful soup; for the winter sunset was dipping a rosy lip to it as I stopped to admire.

It was about here I met Mrs. Hunter in late November and we praised the colours of autumn. We could not see the colours because it was nearly dark. Buff trees across the meadow stood like horses in a monumental patience—or was it that horses were in my mind? Their ghosts follow me all the way from Blacksmith's Corner, where I had regularly stood with them at George's forge. The great buff oak tree over there had that look as of sleep solidified that a great horse has, especially when it is standing with a hind leg half lifted and the hoof edge cutting the turf.

Mrs. Hunter had dismounted from her bike as a flashy car overtook her in the narrow lane. She said it was a lovely time of the year, and my beeches had looked gay as she passed them earlier. I agreed, although you could not see that now. They glowed like embers over us, we knew. We stood awhile in sodden dusk praising November, knowing that brown, red and gold were patterning the trim hedge beside us like the back of a long sofa. All that were visible were sharp white flecks where the opposite hedge had been trimmed; the slips of naked wood like small sudden flames.

'How did you get past the bus?' I asked.

'I had to cram into the bank.' (The lane is sunk there.) 'And how did you get past that combine?'

'I stepped aside into 50 cows' footsteps.'

We said goodnight, and her cycle lamp went flickering along before her. I continued on my way with cheer of heart from all our praise of November. I saw a window aglow, and my wife appeared on the gravel, recognising my tuneless whistle.

'I wondered if you were lying in a ditch somewhere. I was just going to ring Sighile to know if you'd started ...'

'Her kettle was singing so sweetly, and her Black Bryony ...'

'Her what?'

'I call her cat that. She climbs up one's legs to one's lap in a twining sort of way, as a plant climbs. So I call her Black Bryony. Her real name is Bramble; but she sheathes her prickles. She makes impromptu small mia-ows to the tune of the kettle. And then the alarm clock ...'

'Alarm clock?'

'Yes. It suddenly went ting-a-ling-a-ling steadily and slowly; and she said, "My bread." She bakes her bread to an alarm clock. So she bustled up and turned her loaves out of their tins. I like to watch a housewife turn-ing out her bread, slipping out the loaves upside down, and the little tap she gives to their bottoms; a double tap with her knuckles, as you do. And there they sat, golden brown, smelling sweet, smug as cats ...

'And then I met Mrs. Hunter and we stopped and spent ten minutes in the dusk, praising November ...'

'A sodden dusk.'

'A glorious dusk to walk in. I was reciting the *Scholar Gipsy* to myself: "Crossing the stripling Thames at Bab-lock Hythe", as I splashed through the water that had flooded the lane at Blackett Bottom. Mr. Lowe guaran-teed the shoes he sold me were waterproof, and it was the first time I was wearing them. I gazed at the flood;

then strode on boldly. And they were waterproof, though I went in almost up to my ankles ...

'"Crossing the stripling Thames ..." what a grand poem that is for a walker in the dusk, and a light of flame distantly on my left, that should have been "The line of festal light in Christ Church hall", but in fact was a bonfire on the refuse dump in the dingle of Ilketshall St. John ...'

WHY DID one flap of the toaster fall with a crash just as I was transferring an egg balanced on a teaspoon from pan to egg cup? It rolled. I pursued it; luckily it was hard-boiled. And how came fragments of eggshell in my second cup of instant coffee? Never mind; that was last time. On this occasion of her going to house-keep for a daughter-in-law with a newborn babe, my wife arranged with our kind friend Sighile that she would house me and feed me. So now I dwell temporarily at the other end of our lane. I wake to the church tower seen from a different angle. To the post box is a mere stroll. 'Public Footpath' in green enamel points outward from a corner of the churchyard.

On a day last summer I met an American here, in a candy-coloured American holiday jacket and cap. He was photographing a headstone. 'My grandfather and grandmother were married in this church just a hundred and one years ago today,' said his American wife. The name of the grandfather was Green. Greens lie in this churchyard beside the gale-wrung pines that glow bronze at sundown: families of Greens through the centuries.

Now a fresh green sign points us beyond their graves; as if 'Onward to Resurrection.' We stepped into a field of ryegrass, Sighile, and I, and her golden dog.

And beyond that field, whither? Of course there is no 'path'. And I have mislaid my stick in some corner of her house. Sighile thinks we should turn to the left; I think to the right. We go apart in search of 'Footpath'. I look back. She stands with a vast ploughland behind her, whose only motion is a snowstorm of gulls around a distant plough. O my candy-coloured American, you should aim your chromatic camera at what makes English gardens grow, and English lawns look trim, and an English pond, unchoked by sedge, shine clear as a pane of sky—at an English countrywoman, member of the W.I., always 'on the make' not of money but of things woven and things grown and cooked slowly with all their juices conserved. The title of this imagined study in brown—brown hair, brown jumper, brown skirt, before brown ploughland carpeting the view to the horizon —would be at this moment 'Where is the Path?'

I lurch on slippery clover. Sighile exclaims, 'But you've not got your stick!' She seizes an ashplant lying on the verge and tries to break it under her foot. It bends like a bow. She bends with it, wrestles with it, wrists braced. It cracks and slivers. She twists the slivers. The fracture becomes a shock-head of fibres. Round and round she twirls the top end, the other held firm to earth. Just one fibre remains attached. Windmill motions accelerate. It parts. I am handed a staff that looks fixed in a spasm of becoming a serpent.

'Just a beard, and you'd be a prophet.'

I shake my head. 'Raleigh's more the man for me.

"Give me my scallop-shell of quiet, My staff of faith to walk upon".'

We stride on through soaked clover in guaranteed waterproof footwear. 'The long walks that give one fearlessness,' wrote the young Rebecca West. I think she was right.

'Do we go this way now or that way?' Sighile who is ahead calls back. The choice looks to be between a ditch and a swamp. Dog chooses swamp. We follow and reach a road. Another green fingerpost here points straight along the road to St. Margaret's as the crow flies. Surely elves haunt these ancient commons. Last week this fingerpost pointed back to the church whence we had come.

We have come at last to St. Margaret's Church. 'Straight on for butter,' says Sighile. 'Butter?' I query, but already she is leading me through the lych gate and past the tower at whose foot lies buried (another Green) out late pastor. How full the church was for his funeral in that year at primrose time. Doors stood open : people were singing in from outside to swell the singing within. Good pastor; much missed. Once more the thought comes, 'What is death?' Bunyan's Mr. Standfast answers : 'The waters indeed are to the palate bitter, yet the thought of what waits for me on the other side doth lie as a glowing coal at my heart.'

We cross a rustic bridge out of the churchyard over a small watercourse and come in sight of a farmhouse as memoried as the church. The farmer's wife has a trussed fowl ready for my companion. Eggs are ranged in the dairy, and there will be butter 'when our cows begin to calve in January'. So the cream separator hums here of a morning? That is a sound unheard by me since 1928. We talk of butter-churning; the 'flip-flop' or the 'slosh' of butter 'coming' or not coming, devil take it, after changing to the other arm and back how many times.

Now we are walking down Shoe Devil Lane. Who shoed the Devil here? Some Faustian blacksmith perhaps, and for what purpose, when myth once hazed old England like a morning mist? On either side stretch the flat dark ploughlands of the 'Saints'. Sunset clouds lie ruddy and slender on the horizon's rim, as we enter that home where we are invited to high tea, and wheat wine, and barley wine, and elderberry and gooseberry wine. It is a feast of the home-made and the home-grown; which is the way we live and try to live. The wine bottles glow more richly than those glass jorums in chemists' windows which charmed me as a child. One has elderberry, I try wheat wine, another chooses barley wine. The limpid dyes of nature tempt us. We grow merry. But I talk too much. I always do. I lingered even after Sighile was beyond the parlour door. 'Next time you must bring a pair of scissors,' did I hear our hostess advise her?

'To clip my tongue?' I asked Sighile. She did not say no. I am contrite; I am humble. Next time I will look people in the eyes and not orate to the ceiling. I will ask meekly and wait for an answer. The little boy in me will not show off, I vow to myself. Next time. But will there be a next time? It was the wheat wine. Yes, of course. But an inner voice cries, 'The fault, dear Brutus, is not in wheat wine, but in yourself that you are garrulous.'

And yet—we went straight on to another party and I ate an avocado pear swimming in unctuous sauce on a flat plate on my lap and did not spill a drop. Sober enough. No excuses. Be humbled. It's good for you.

❧ ❧ ❧ ❧ ❧ ❧

IT WAS another party, and there were pot-holes. It was at the end of a long driftway to the marshes, where gulls tilted their wings seaward, and rooks to landward were 'scouring the pot' as they call it in Suffolk—that is to say, spiralling up and up till they were black motes, scouring the pot of the sky. As we neared the old house in the dusk, there were pot-holes, black and brimming, moonshiny. I rejoiced. Pot-holes act like a charm against Planners, even as crossed sticks ward off the devil.

There were many people in the house when we got there. Yet, how quiet it was. There was wine on tap; yet how quiet. If it had been the usual 'drinks party' everybody by now would have been talking at the tops of their voices. Yes, I have heard the roar in a country house even while approaching through the park. But these people, clad with a sort of absent-minded grace, were talking quietly and naturally. When they laughed they did not go off like a parcel bomb. That truebred East Anglian guffaw (even before the joke is through) can pin you to the wall.

A man with a white beard held a stick of celery by its upper shoots, balanced between two fingers, while he talked to a girl who was like the young Dorelia of Augustus John. In his right hand he held a piece of

French roll cleft with soft white cheese, with disks of cucumber erect along it, making of it a new white creature with a green backbone. And the celery dangled from those crisply curled shoots hung on his fingers, vibrating slightly in time with a small guitar which a man crouched in a corner was using as the murmur of his *alter ego*. The while I was talking to people my eyes dwelt on that celery stick, blanched and sheer, then escaping into fronds of gold and green. What is art? I asked myself; for this meeting was about the arts. Art is doing a thing because you enjoy to do it, I concluded, as I watched the celery stalk. What a thing it was; forced and blanched, but at the top, how nature insists to flow and curl.

The meeting was of the 'East Anglian Arts Trust' (for which read, people). There was shown a film of Barsham Faire. Once more we were in high summer watching the great maypole being canti-levered erect. We heard again the bells of Barsham Church beside the Glebe, saw wood smoke billowing up where viands were roasting.

Dancers leaped, sages meditated; each to his own device. See again the hautboy player, how his lips looked like a red rose pursed around his pipe, and his red hair and beard aflame like Sol in a picture. I even caught a glimpse of myself, a recumbent form in the camera's eye for a second, also our friend Sighile in her green gown sitting behind her wares.

And for this year? Will there be, not only a summer faire on Barsham Glebe, but also a 'Bungay May Fair'?

'Bungay May Fair' was once famous as the day for turning cattle out to grass. By then they were knee-deep in it and buttercups. Out they were driven, with a 'Hup-

102

ho!', and a 'Turn 'em, will you?' as a terrified stranger
found a herd of horn frisking with spring madness toward him on the road. 'Turn 'em!' was a common cry
in the country to anyone meeting beasts at full gallop:
also in market towns as a heifer or two set off down the
high street with twirling tails. Say what you will, life
was fun at Bungay May Fair time, and the new rich
yellow spring butter was seen in the market, and how
come it that Mrs. Fizzle's made top price that week in the
auction and not Mrs. Bossom's as was usual? Spiteful
mutterings, gleeful grins. I had walked, with string in
my boots, driving seven steers to market.

I have just read how in villages the farm men and
rural artificers have been replaced by a generation of
professional commuters, with hands less useful than
leaves on a tree. And how Norwich now produces little
but offices and clerks in cubicles. I walked but a short
way there yesterday and glanced in windows. Teacups
and specifications, teacups and invoices, teacups and
girls at typewriters: how can all this barren life be sus-
tained that shuttles between Norwich and everywhere
around Norwich, producing only paper? For one potato
grown, how many typewritten, stencilled, duplicated
sheets? It's awful to contemplate, this Paradise of Planners, with interim reports for fig-leaves.

Thank God for pot-holes, and the sweet low thrum
of a plucked string and a tremulous pipe; and our host
doing a private dance of his own to them, the while a
great green rocking-fowl conveyed two young boys to-
and-fro in time with this low breeze of music, to which
Dorelia stirred as in a waft of air off water, or that scurry
which crimps the light of a lake. And the stick of cel-

ery, swinging by its curled fronds, became a thing of art, a process, a pendulum of the counter-revolution, for which I have been looking ever since I fled the threat of 'Progress' 50 years ago to get me 30 acres of clay and two horses and a wooden plough, and whistled to keep myself in company while I learned to live.

Although I did not know these Arts-Trust people personally, I came to feel at home among them, rather 'liberated' in fact. Liberated from what? That is a big question. Perhaps Whitman best answers it: 'I loaf and invite my soul.' Yes, I loafed and invited my soul. Thereupon little impulses spring up like grass after rain. I danced next morning to a Dvorak concerto (at least sketched a sort of dance with my feet on my study carpet). 'Music that cannot be danced to or sung to, is not music.' (To this a music critic musingly said there was something to be said for it.) So I didn't exactly loaf, did I? Nor do they.

I wish fairs could spring up wherever there are glebes and commons to barter the work of men's hands. When money is extinct and assembly lines have halted for ever, we shall have to rely on barter and affection to turn misery to music. To be able actually to taste a potato would be a first thawing of the cramp of our open-prison bureaucracy—to judge between an Arran Pilot for instance, which has a soul, and the lately trumpeted Desirée which tastes of nothing and is fit only for Marvel-Mash.

Slump to Salvation? On with the Counter Revolution.

AT A W.I. meeting about the Christmas party there was a suggestion from the chair that we came masked, wearing dominoes.

This proposal was greeted (my wife says) with an uncertain silence, broken at last by milady in a clear, loud voice: 'Rather awkward for those wearing glasses.' That kiboshed it.

'Surely,' I said to her later, 'people could have made up their minds whether to wear their dominoes inside or outside their glasses.'

'Dear husband,' she rejoined, 'if you think for one moment that you would not be instantly recognisable in a domino you are indeed illusion-prone. Your walk, your voice, your habit of patting your right-hand pocket as if expecting a fairy gift ...'

'We could at least have pretended ...' I muttered.

But next morning all was cheer except the weather. With secateurs and old but undefeated gloves, we set out. In a certain yard stood waist-high edifices in the form of prisms of willow, airily criss-cross, looking white and classical; also huge primeval trunks that reminded me of crocodiles. The prisms of willow carved from these were to become cricket bats. Further within this area were to be found Christmas trees for sale. What have Christmas trees to do with cricket bats: 'Only connect,' E. M. Forster said.

Leaning against some of the thousands of Christmas trees on December 25th, you may be sure will be a boy's first adult cricket bat, not only here but probably in the

Antipodes too (where they can't grow such willows). These bats when complete will bear the indelible hammer-mark of this old firm in the Waveney Valley.

I wondered which of the embryos before me was destined to be carried to clapping and cheers, having earned its player a century at Lord's or Down Under?

Next we looked in at The Fleece to wish ourselves the compliments of the season, milady wearing her hussar fur hat. It was lunch hour, the company jolly. Our order was double stout and ginger wine. 'It warms the cockles,' she said. 'Are you sure?' I asked. She was sure. I took a sip. 'Yes,' I agreed, 'something seems to warm something,' and returned to my black draught.

Then out into the byways of the country in a blustering wind. We came to a spinney where ivy trailed from blackthorn trunks in a green winter mock-up of beribboned maypoles. Ivy, tough favourite of nature, creates its own motif. These trailers we gathered by the armful. When we wanted to move on we found we were treading on each other's ivy trains. We came to a stand, ivy-enwound. There is a picture by Aubrey Beardsley of men being turned into vines by dryads, or nymphs by satyrs—his sexes are never altogether clear to me. 'Are we growing leafy hands?' I asked. 'Your ivy trails have bound me fast.' 'Yours me,' she answered. 'We must unwind.' 'Must we?' I the illusion-prone asked, as I wrestled in green bonds without wanting to break them.

We tried turning clockwise, which tightened them; then anti-clockwise, and at last we were free. We took each a wide circuit and arrived at the car, and packed it with our booty.

On a steep bank stood a giant elm laden with bunches

of large-leaved ivy bustling in the gale. We hooked it, we dragged. Surely the tree was grateful to be a little less burdened, fledged with ivy as with preened green plumage, a rainwear most redundant to that griggled bark. We fell down the bank as ivy gave way, picked ourselves up and it, and filled the car. Next some yew, some laurel, some holly from home paddocks; all the green life that sleeps not in winter.

'The pre-Christmas rush.' A bane on the civic ads whose god is Shopping and the altar of their sacred grove a checkout. This was our country version of it; great store of festive leaves, some like hands, some lean green stars; wealth of earth-grown green 'leather', and we not a penny the worse off.

The big leaves flapped, but the small ones clung with a passionate pertinacity to the bark, faintly incised there where lovers once recorded their initials. There was a small dry 'Tch-Tch' sound as we peeled off the small ivy to wreathe with it the old school bell in the village hall for our Christmas party.

The Church in ancient times forbade the decorating of houses with ivy. It was pagan, said the Church; it was Druidic; it was called the Bacchic Weed. Well, it's to be a wine and cheese party; and I am merry and unregenerate when I raise the glass of cheer. But only we two who gathered it will know how passionately it clung to its tree, when it shall be seen loosely wreathing the old school bell—the infant hands of the small ivy that clung in gales and rain and exclaimed at being parted from the rough old bark, and revealed the smudged initials of some forgotten tryst, even as our walnut tree does.

Suddenly the air was a riot of snowflakes, tickling our faces, settling on milady's hat like the retreat from Moscow. Where's our troika? In, up and away, cracking imaginary whip over imaginary steeds; Kitty, Boxer, Prince, who rush with us past the ruined forge, swing round Blacksmith's Corner, full gallop ...

Oh, has our troika become just one small car? It was that scent of balsam exuding from the cloud of evergreens. If pumpkin into coach for under-privileged kitchen maid, why not car into troika for fur-hatted gatherers of evergreens in the snow? Illusionist! Life is real, life is earnest. No. It's all a blessed miracle. Look at this one ivy leaf—and think of the moon.

❧ ❧ ❧ ❧ ❧ ❧

DECEMBER 1ST, Christmas pudding stirabout; 'Although it's not Stir-up Sunday,' said our hostess. Whereupon I parroted, 'Stir up, we beseech Thee O Lord, the wills of Thy faithful people ...' None caught on to what I was quoting, not having been disciplined year in year out by such a stern old school as mine where we had every collect and epistle of the Church's year drummed into us. Indeed I am thankful for it in that I could recall those wonderful collects: 'Stir up, we beseech Thee ...' and '... forasmuch as without Thee we are not able to please Thee ...' as I stirred the goo of dough and candied fruit, with a whole yolk of egg trembling and drowning in it at the prod of my spoon; a ceremony followed by bumpers of wine in which we toasted the Christmas month.

Next, it was we who gave a party. ('Pound hits all-

108

time low.' Yes, and it did in 1931; and here we two are still, owing no man. So what?) Our party was for 'The Lane'. My wife brewed a barrel of beer. Christine made sausage rolls of a size to be encompassed in one bite; a boon to a crumb-dropper like me. Sighile made mince pies. I told her I did not eat mince pies, because they do not agree with me. I must eat one of hers, she said. I did eat one; and then I ate another, and they did agree with me.

After that, there was a Christmas party in the village hall. The festoons of ivy we had gathered looked so natural draped around the old school bell that they might have grown there. Fixing two sprigs of holly over the clock, Sighile said, 'They must not look like two ears.' I held a chair steady. Even so, there was a jiggle somewhere that found its way from the floor to her hands. At last the sprigs did not, she judged, look like ears.

('Shares hit 20-year low'). But sugar-beet was the preoccupation of our lane here and now. The party was as good as a harvest-home for one neighbour : he had finished carting his that very day. I had watched all December as I passed the family team surely eroding the acreage with beet knives by hand, on soaked ground in which no machine would work.

A lady was demonstrating how to decorate a yule log. In her hands was a big maincrop potato. She transfixed it on a spike protruding from the log. I winced for that spud, and momentarily averted my eyes. 'How's your beet-lifting getting on?' I asked of the seat behind me in a whisper meant to be pianissimo, but which came out of me like a breeze in sere grass.

'Only needed another half-hour,' its occupant heart-

109

ily breathed back. 'But for that storm ...'

'This potato is the base for our design,' the lady was saying. Some winged-looking adornments, with secret spikes under them, were pressed down on that potato; one, two, three.

'Oh!' I groaned. 'Is it your sciatica?' muttered my wife.

'No—that poor spud: I feel for it.' How hard I had tried not to impale my potatoes; and shuddered at finding one of the best coming up on the prongs of my fork.

A few red-spotted toadstools were applied to one end of the log; and I thought of Celia. Why Celia? Because we had walked love-lorn in woods, gazed into brown pools and at red-spotted toadstools. How I had loved her. How my mother hated her. 'That woman!' she hissed. Ah, the pains of youth.

'Ouch!' A cardinal-red candle was spiked on to that now beauty-smothered Majestic spud. Alas, poor spud: I had just read a book which claimed vegetable life has feelings. There now, light the red candle. A meek nut-shaped flame blooms out of it, and points the charm of the whole design. Applause. Now a carol.

Now tables are being unfolded. Here comes wine, red and white: crusty bread, soft cheese flavoured with chives.

'What do you see in your wine?' asks my wife, seeing my eyes peering closely at it.

'That little ruby star, d'you see, where it focuses all the light in the hall.' Once I wrote to Celia, 'You are the glow within the wine,' and my mother found the letter. 'That woman!'

I raise my glass to Sighile (about whom Chaucer could

have written a tale). 'Here's to you and your four "hennes"; Pertelote, Proudfoot, Justapeck and Prate.'

'Bandog killed Prate, so now there be but treye—and Prate, alas, alack, was in full lay.'

(Try being Chaucer: it seems dead easy.) Suddenly the lights go out. 'Is this the Mystery Number?' I ask my wife, who with me recalls those certain moments in the dances of the Twenties when the lights were dimmed and you found yourself dancing with a beautiful Unknown, her bobbed hair tickling your face. 'Ashes of Roses', that was the scent. This elephant never forgets.

But it's only a blown fuse.

❧ ❧ ❧ ❧ ❧ ❧

ON NEW Year's Day I had paused to observe how almost golden the branches of my weeping willow were, drifting like long hair in the breeze. I felt a warmth on the nape of my neck. It was the sun. I turned, blinked a moment at that vast bonfire in space 93,000,000 miles away, that could yet waft a sense of warmth to my neck on January 1st.

It suddenly seemed extraordinary to me that that blazing thing should be floating there and we dependent on it for everything, and yet for most of our time we take no notice of it, unless we are package tour operators, when we advertise it as shining perpetually somewhere else; 'plus the loveliest women in the world', as one advertisement added.

That same sun the other evening produced such a splendour in its going down as I never before remember. The whole sky was aglow: white cottages to the east were coloured by it: high elms held it in a mesh just as they took a rime frost one morning, but now pink. It was as if some rich alloy were hammered across the west, rent with glimpses of a promised land. It stands in my mind still like an empire awaiting the ability to colonise it; or as the author of 'The Cloud of Unknowing' says: 'to touch divers souls with the grace of contemplation.'

The oak boughs angling for the emergent stars were black, but the light never seemed to die out of that sky.

I sat waiting for the dark: but even when that cloud directly overhead glowed no more there was a wealth of distilled daylight in the air. When I switched on a light the whole window went black. There is no darkness in nature. I recalled that hour which we used to call 'between the lights', as we sat conversing before we lit a candle.

The sun, I am told, 'is quite a small star', which disappears and reappears to us, and we call it tomorrow, though it looks just like today come back again. What is tomorrow; and why do people grow old?

※　　※　　※　　※　　※　　※

HERE WE are at 4 p.m., blessed with 20 minutes' more daylight than on Christmas Day. Sunset flush pulses faintly through a counterpane of cloud. Cows begin to heave themselves toward the gateway to milking. Foreshortened, their bellies look globular behind their wedge-shaped heads. A lot goes on in those four stomachs before one drop of milk goes 'ting' in a pail.

'Come on.' That command floats across the pasture. All ingoings and outgoings along our lane are sodden. There is no cure for this in a winter of deluge, when green fodder must be carted daily from field to milking herd. 'Mud on Road.' How can mud not be on road? First sugar beet carting; now, just carting for cows. Tractor wheel ruts, liquescent, are canals of the sky, pink with sunset, in which the slow cows are reflected upside down.

Cows and tractors wallow, mankind plods, hens flap-doodle. Mud lies heaved into forms like crocodiles asleep. Two Muscovy ducks sit watching perpetually seven Aylesbury ducks on a pond ploughing the surface into silvery arrows which broaden behind them and disappear; so they wheel and ruffle it into quicksilver again in the reverse direction. The Muscovies just sit and watch, the bits of red on their foreheads making them look quietly angry. An awkward corner of the sign-posted 'Public Footpath' has been ploughed since last I plodded it. A biped must balance for several yards on an erect crested furrow beside a wet and yawning ditch. Buttressed by my staff I achieve it.

Bless the small birds, unaware of mud: they flit, flit, flit. How nimble they are. They feed upside down, pecking into bags of nuts hung for them. They tap on the old lady's window. Once, mistaking the house, they tapped on mine. She has a feeding table and swaying half-coconuts, so close to her window you could touch her guests' plumage if there were not glass there. To one who is immobile and lives in one room they are life. One might subside into a static old age: any of us might. I take heed of the serenity of this lady. What was it Keats said, musing on the view from his window? 'I become the sparrow pecking the gravel.'

Should I, if made immobile, be granted proxy freedom by these great and blue tits, their darting flight, through watching them all every day? What is happiness? It is the doll a poor child made from a few rags. I recall being set fast by sciatica. I envied every limb that swung. Amazingly time did not drag: the days flew by in one continual curve, not divided into hours as the days of busy men. I stared at birds, at fuchsias, like dancers in air, at anything that stirred in a breeze. I look at the crowd of tits in my nut tree and wonder if their activity could sustain my involuntary stillness? I think of it frequently: I have my example in our lane.

As I walked on, still active enough to balance on a crested furrow, I saw Sighile with a skep crossing her gravel. She called: 'You're just in time to help me fetch down my apples from the loft.'

Her 'loft' is a platform resting on the cross beams of her garage, an ingenious device. Who knows how to use space to better advantage than she does? I climb the ladder, she stands below, resting the skep on her shoulder. I hand down the apples two at a time: Bramley's Seedlings with a cool sub-acid aroma; their skins feel almost tacky. When the skep is full I ease it from her back. We carry it in. She puts them in her pantry, in which everything is packed so precisely that there seems not room for even one thing more. But she stoops there, her back to me; when she emerges from it, they are all packed away in there—somewhere.

Her alarm clock rings slowly: ting-ling-ling. 'Time to turn the potatoes,' she says. She opens a door of her stove: potatoes are baking in their jackets in the ashpan. She turns them over; shuts the door: opens the oven door. Here two Bramleys are baking, dates pushed into the top of each. Their skins have shrunk, exposing a level line of white and fluffy flesh between bodice and skirt as it were. The skins are turning amber, sweating juice. But they have not lost their figures.

As I walked homeward down the lane I recalled a poem by one of the Georgian poets of my youth, about apples lying in a loft. The moon peeps in through a small window: the poet has never forgotten those 'moon-washed apples of wonder'.

I only remember the last line of that poem. But I remember it well. I think how the big Bramleys in Sighile's loft may have shone there, as they did on their tree through many summer nights; 'moon-washed apples of wonder.'

❋ ❋ ❋ ❋ ❋ ❋

WHEN PEOPLE ask me where I dwell, I tell them, 'I am on the way to the Saints.' And when I add that there are angels among the Saints, they think I am a visionary. But it is true. The parish of St. Andrew is the next I set foot upon when I go outside my door; and beyond St. Andrew's are the Saint-named villages of Ilketshall and South Elmham. An angel of St. Andrew stands in my house. I rather worship her. I often ask her what I should think or what I should do. And listen.

I know that thou shalt not bow down to any graven image; but my angel is not graven: she is woven of straw by a lady of St. Andrew's. A quibble? Just one of many which have floated me through life.

When I tell my friends I dwell with my angel on the way to the Saints, they imagine some sort of Eden, or tap their foreheads. Let them. St. Andrew's Great Common is a sort of Eden if you are in the mood. The lane over Great Common is high and dry. I have walked toward some of the finest sunsets I have ever seen over Great Common; even more splendid than the streaky-bacon dawns that greet my drawing back the curtains on High Common.

In a sodden dusk Great Common can be moody, gipsy-ish: all black and green and hay-coloured bents. As darkness falls its bramble bushes seem to coagulate: its sloe thickets look blue-black, impenetrable. A photograph of the 1930s shows it clear of bushes, pasturing horses. Now it is an unthrifty common; a raggle-taggle place. I passed a black square whence a dunghill has been carted; yet enough remained to have fertilised all my potato patch. I then had a thrifty thought for that which the forklift tractor rolls over, but which a man with handfork and barrow could have garnered.

'Does any bird eat sloes, however hard up?' I asked my companion. 'Are sloes any use at all?'

'For sloe jelly with hare,' came the answer; 'and for sloe gin.' And she went on to praise sloe gin. 'It has a particular "tang", an aroma, a ... Let's get on, and I'll pour you a nip. Keeps out the damp, you know, therapeutic. I could almost bless the damp.'

We were soon marching. 'Look at that sky over Bungay: just look at it.'

'Yes, it will look even better from my west window atop of Mill Common.'

116

Thus my friend praised sloe gin; even looked with affection at the hunched blue-black forms of the sloe bushes we were passing.

True, the sky was all embers from this west window, and sloe gin was a clear rose colour in the glass.

What says the great herbalist Gerard of the virtues of the sloe? In a potion it is 'cooling and drying'. But I don't want cooling and drying: I am much too cool and dry as I am. What next? 'Eases all manner of gnawings in the stomach.'

I'll ask my angel. She helps to ease 'all manner of gnawings in my stomach', which are not digestive, but are fears for our finest dreams of trust and patience being strumpeted by moments of crude nature.

It is a very special wheat from the straw of which the lady of St. Andrew's weaves her little angels; a descendant of the bearded wheat which originated geographically in what is known to have been the Garden of Eden; the primitive 'Emmer' which was harvested with a flint sickle in Jericho. So I can think of the angel on my mantelshelf as woven into history, even prehistory.

In Bronowski's 'Ascent of Man' is pictured a little figurine from Jericho of ten thousand years ago. It is of a boy and girl making love. They are cuddled together, compact as a parcel; a human sheaf. Alone there in the outback of time, on the edge of the physical desert, they sowed and reaped their bearded wheat, and loved. Look down at them in their vast solitude, warmed only by their tiny mutual flame, with cries of 'Ah, my love'—vocables equivalent to these in the speech of ancient Jericho. Before the Bible existed, to instruct us what was mortal sin and what was lawful love; long before St. Paul preached about marrying or burning, were these two parcelled up together in their moment of love, the instant of all our tomorrows, even as their wheat was the begetter of our bread.

Since then, what great Churchmen there have been; what Schoolmen, Desert Fathers, Prophets, Prelates; what vows of love enjoined, what betrayals of love by psychological subtleties 'justified'. What lawyers' fees amassed, what semi-orphan children bandied to and fro. Look down again from our office-block civilisation on these two, having no God of ours to compassion them, nor hope of a Christian heaven; only their small fervid flame, and no wit but to love and suckle, to winnow and make loaves.

But now my road descends from Great Common and rejoins our lane as I approach the parish of St. John's.

❦ ❦ ❦ ❦ ❦ ❦

ALL WINTER Mill Lane has worn a winking skin of water. We walk under the elms from which we gathered the big-leaved ivy for our Christmas party. We are now in the parish of St. John, and come in sight of the sand pit. As a school-girl Mrs. Watkin and her friends (including London children on holiday) were every summer taken for a day trip to the seaside. Thereafter, on fine days, her mother would do up a picnic lunch and they would take their buckets and spades to the sand pit, and there play at being by the seaside, sitting in a bay of bright sand. This sand was sold for a shilling a tumbril-load, for the benefit of the church. Mrs. Watkin has lived since a small child in the former Rectory beside the church.

We approach the sand pit. That golden imaginary seaside of the children of yesterday has become a municipal dump. It is littered with derelict domestic iron and paper and rags. It is a perpetual smoking Gehenna. And it is a Palais des Rats for ever.

Sand pits have been beloved of artists like Munnings, who painted grey horses in their golden light. Beloved also of children wherein to re-enact their day by the sea. But today I can show you only squalor; a gangrenous pock mark amid smiling nature.

Let's get on, if we can get past this Slough of Despond. Bunyan, thou shouldst be living at this hour. Now we are nearing the end of our crinkum-crankum lane, from Barsham Glebe to Ilketshall St. John, bordered by fruitful fields and winking overflows, by last summer's willow-herb, now a tangle of rich tobacco hue, by new primroses, a daring sheep's parsley in full flower in February, and herb robert already peeping its small red flower round a root. I walk this lane in all weathers, all seasons, sometimes light of heart (oddly most cheerful when the rain has been beating a tattoo on my mac).

A bevy of fowl is waiting by the coachyard of the old Rectory as if expecting us. Their king is a gay Chanticleer—'gay' in old Suffolk meaning 'many-coloured'. His throat is mottled white and yellow, bronze his back, blue-black as wet ink his tail feathers, springy as the curled bells that still hang on the wall in St. John's Rectory. He crows. His silken-plumed rival crows in answer: they stand beak to beak, necks rippling upward to

119

utter their cockadoodledoos, the two gay ones. They stamp, they strut: the one with the tallest comb is king, and he knows it.

The hens are thrilled: they flutter excitedly at being attended by these cocks, and by lesser cocks playing at spurred chivalry to any who will attend, even the bantam. There are broad brown hens in full sail, small perky darting hens, white hens, black hens, speckled hens. Says the lady of the house, 'One of them will disappear, then weeks later reappear with a brood.' This plumed commune perpetuates itself as nature does. No advertised 'Free Range' is as free as theirs.

We move on toward the church: the birds escort us, making every sort of sound that can issue from the beak of fowl: murmur, croon, prate, cackle, doodledoo. They veer into a meadow. Royal Chanticleer halts every few yards to cockadoodledoo with draughty flappings. He cannot crow without flapping his wings, nor flap without crowing, it seems. This slows him. The rest are already scattered about the field, beaks to earth, presenting a series of pointed sterns.

Now we are abreast of the church: its slender tower is a look-out at the very furthest point of our lane. It overlooks the 'turnpike' as we in the country still call it; a Roman road; Stone Street; a marching road once, then a trotting road, and when cars came in, an accident spot. Now traffic swirls in a wide arc at a safe distance.

We climb an uphill lane behind the church until we are level with its weather-vane. All around lie sweeps of tillage. Blown smoke from a hedger's fire alternately veils and unveils the trees of the Glebe. How old, how English, how fecund a prospect: good tillage, gay cocks and hens ... Ah, but the sand pit, the children's 'seaside', now a Gehenna.

Forget it. The wild strawberry that creeps under the churchyard gate is already showing the white faces of its tiny flowers.

※ ※ ※ ※ ※ ※

ONE DAY I shall write a book about those parishes which are known as 'The Saints', because each one is named after a saint, and there are two St. Margarets. Most of them have commons, which are wild, and haunted by ghosts of wandering men. In one of them was found a Nuremberg trading token of the 13th century.

Sometimes I sit in one of their small churches and feel the spirit of these 'Saints' very strongly: they are sad, in the way that human life is sad, since it ends in a headstone; but where love is, noble as an epitaph.

I think that to me St. Michael's is the most lovely. Lovely? I do not know how to define 'beauty' in that sense. But it has a spirit, wildish as the wind that bloweth where it listeth, and bloweth around the tiny church reached by a grass track across its common. The wind outside the church has a voice: the silence within that church is also to me a voice, that murmurs like a shell held to the ear. I tread a pavement tomb of a squire who is designated 'Gent.': he has lain here since the seventeen hundreds.

What there is about this church I could not explain, with its simple cross made out of two rods of hazel; a cross startlingly light to handle for so profound a message. In this whitewashed one-room cottage of God I feel that the destinies of our passion-tossed hearts are determined. Here I have a clue to the code of our lives, even if no more than that they have a clue, and we live in a parable. So that I even wonder idly, is there another meaning to that milk churn standing in the porch, glimmering like pewter in the gloaming? Holy water? Grace? Treasure?

Once I saw traces of confetti, not blackthorn petals— or were they?—around the wicket gate, whose click and scrape I have come to know. And on an evening when the sky wore tinted cloudlets which reflected through the clear east window on the walls with a flush of pink, I sat in shadow at the end of a pew, thinking— or not thinking: there is hardly a word for what the state of being is of one who sits here when the place is empty and the Bible on the lectern stands silently eloquent.

I heard a light tread. I did not turn my head, expecting a verger's voice to utter a 'Good evening' and break my spell. I feared that voice; which told me how much this silence meant to me, oppressed at that time with certain personal forebodings. No voice uttered, but the light tread persisted. There passed me a boy and a girl; hardly more than schoolchildren I guessed. They did not notice me: they were concerned only with each other. They were not just straying: they had not flowers for the altar. Nothing of that sort.

They halted at the altar rails, and stood staring at the warm clouds through the east window. Then the girl took something out of her screwed handkerchief which she handed to the boy. He took it. It glittered slightly:

it looked to me like a trinket. I did not move my head lest I alarm them, only my eyes. It looked like a thimble. The boy took her left hand in his and slipped it on to her fourth finger. They turned their faces to each other, and kissed silently with closed lips. It was passionless, yet it was not a peck, more like the application of a seal. They stood quite still: they did not utter. Then hand-in-hand they walked back down the aisle, their feet making a sound like the tapping of a light tack into a shoe.

They had no eyes for this stranger in the shadow. I turned my head now that they were past. The nave was growing dim with dusk. They might have been ghosts but for their footsteps, which I heard, or seemed to hear. Was I the ghost, I almost wondered, disembodied by certain sad thoughts of my own? I thought of the two children in Henry James's ghost story. 'The Turn of the Screw'. But there was no hint of menace here, but as naïve a teenagers' troth as children would plight with a trinket out of a cracker.

I went into the porch and saw them drifting away in the dusk which held yet a trace of afterglow. Had they left bicycles by the road? I saw two red lights gliding away. Who were they, I wondered? Were they acting some wedding at which they had been present?

I sat down in the porch of the church on St. Michael's common, and recalled a girl friend I had when I was 15. Our parents were amused to see our eyes gazing into each other's in long moments at a party. But I do not smile at the recollection even now; least of all now. I still reckon it as a gift of grace, or trust; her green eyes gazing; those eyes filling all my mind, as my eyes filled hers.

I forget her name. No, wait a moment: Eileen, that was her name. Eileen who? Never mind; see only the green irises of the eyes. We had nothing to say then, too shy even to utter. We sat through party noises in a reserved silence. It was a first offering of ourselves, the more touching that we did not yet possess ourselves or know ourselves. Yet we gave ourselves in silence between the explosions of crackers. She had donned a hollow crown, and I some sort of bonnet. We went on staring, bonnet and crown, in the enchantment which had fallen on us.

Here in the church porch, now quite dark, I recalled that the boy, after he had put the thimble on the girl's finger, took from his pocket a pebble-like piece of abraded sea-green glass, and both looked at it. All life is a code, I told myself. A fragment of glass which has washed around the oceans of the world, is picked up by a teen-ager and becomes a talisman of two who have 'married' with a thimble. I do not laugh at it: it could have an equivalent at any age to those for whom life is still a parable. I watch middle-aged people in the street. Just occasionally, as yesterday, I see a middle-aged man fold his wife's middle-aged hand in his, lead her across the street and keep hold of it as they tread the pavement of the other side. But of all the other couples who walk with daylight between them, I sometimes ask myself, when did the touching cease?